CHERNOBYL

CHERNOBYL

ANDREY ILLESH

RICHARDSON & STEIRMAN, INC.

NEW YORK

CONTENTS

IN PLACE OF A FOREWORD

I t was Sunday evening in Moscow. The train for Kiev chugged smoothly away from the platform. There were very few passengers on the platform, or anywhere in the station, and there were very few on the train. But among the few who were aboard, one could feel a hidden tension: the Council of Ministers of the USSR had announced an accident in the fourth reactor at the Chernobyl Nuclear Power Plant.

The Council's first, spare phrases had given rise to anxiety, since it was clear that nothing like it—nothing of such extraordinary gravity—had ever happened before in the Soviet Union. It would be hard to predict what was going to happen next.

Today, a year after the tragic morning of April 26, 1986, after my trip to Chernobyl, my work there, my meetings with hundreds of people, gathering information about what happened, carefully studying everything that my fellow reporters have written about the tragedy at the power plant, I have concluded that this book is a historical necessity warranted by the fact that I saw what went on with my own eyes; by the fact that I've accumulated a body of knowledge about it; by the fact that, bit by bit, I've evaluated what went on; and by the fact that, bit by bit, I've come to certain conclusions.

From today's perspective, the events at Chernobyl will not always match the reports that were issued during the first days of the calamity.

That's to be expected. The unprecedented nature of what

1

happened made it impossible at the time to say certain things with clarity and precision.

What happened?

Who was to blame?

What of the aftermath?

Dozens of the world's greatest experts—scientists with worldwide reputations—came to Chernobyl, to the immediate vicinity of the towering reactor, while it was still charred, half-destroyed, and dangerous. Those very experts came up against incredible problems, thousands of them at once, that not only were complex, but raised difficult, unanswerable questions for the first time anywhere.

It wasn't possible at the time to answer many of the technical questions categorically with a simple yes or no. Instead, at least in the most complicated areas, answers began to take shape only in the course of actually dealing with the accident's aftermath.

With every passing day, more and more of the nation's best brains—its best builders, engineers, and scientists, aided by their most powerful technologies—gathered at the Chernobyl plant, a relatively small area defined by an eighteen-mile radius from the site of the reactor, from which the entire population had been evacuated. Everything that was required in Chernobyl was concentrated there immediately. If some use could be found for people with particular experience or knowledge, or even for their decisiveness, those people were flown in from thousands of miles away. Beginning literally with the first minutes after the accident, the rescue work went on without a break, in multiple shifts, day and night.

And so, what was it like?

In what way can we now say that Reactor No. 4, emitting a terrible and invisible death, has been entombed?

Are the prospects for the life of the plant and the area around it clear?

Has the lesson—and this is terribly important—of the Chernobyl tragedy been fully learned?

In order to comment, I will try leafing through the entries in my journal, listening again to my tape recordings of interviews, meeting again with the hundreds of people, while tracing the key events, one after the other, beginning with the first day, hour, and minute, that were occurring just eighty miles from the millions of people in Kiev.

For the record, these entries can't in any way be considered complete or exhaustive; for any reporter to have talked with everyone who worked on the aftermath of the accident would have been impossible. The eighteen-mile desert zone of Chernobyl was virtually overrun with specialists who'd come there from all over the USSR.

In the crucial events—at the nuclear power plant, in Chernobyl, then in Kiev, and later in Moscow—I was able to participate. What I saw on the scene, and what I reported on daily to the eight million readers of my newspaper, as well as the interviews I conducted with government leaders and scientists, and even medical specialists who came here from abroad, have become, collectively, the basis for this book.

Even when I was first giving thought to the kind of book I wanted to write, it seemed to me very important to respond to what I found being written in some Western newspapers about our calamity. A good deal of what was written, especially during the first days of the tragedy, simply lacked integrity. I saw firsthand how facts can be turned on their heads and how truth can be twisted.

I talked at length with a colleague of mine from France; he wanted to know what the doctors had done and what had happened to the firemen. I tried to help him as best I could. When I finally chanced to read what appeared under this reporter's byline, I was taken aback. Our conversation, in the presence of an interpreter, excluded any possibility of misinterpretation—yet the story was totally false.

First, he made me out to be the editor-in-chief of *Izsvestiya*. Then a nurse—whom, it was clear to me, he'd never seen—had somehow become his chief source of information on the status of the injured. (The story contained dozens of inaccuracies.)

I'm not talking, by the way, about a minor publication, but of the famous *Paris Match*. In the past I thought *Paris Match* deserving of my professional respect, but I found this publication, like others, publishing a stream of fiction.

It is not worth getting into debates with so-called colleagues who are capable of taking pleasure in another person's tragedy.

How well I remember my own reaction, and that of my family and friends, when we watched the tapes of the American shuttle on TV. We froze, watching the screen. We saw the take-off of an ordinary shuttle. And suddenly—the explosion. The instantaneous deaths of the astronauts. Americans weeping, choking with grief. Well, we too had lumps in our throats; we too had tears in our eyes as we watched that tragedy.

At the time, I was sure that that was the only possible reaction to human tragedy—that is, if you're a human being.

I would expect that, in like manner, the events at Chernobyl also brought forth from most of the inhabitants of the planet the natural reaction of grief.

I hope that the person who takes up this book will travel the road to Chernobyl, not just for the sake of getting a glimpse of the earth after a nuclear explosion, but with the expectation of understanding the misfortune that befell his neighbors.

1

THE NUCLEAR POWER PLANT:
April 26, 1986, 1:23 A.M.

Hardly any time had elapsed since the moment of the meltdown, yet here I was, already hurrying toward the scene of the accident. I'd taken the train from Moscow to Kiev. There in Kiev, the capital of the Ukraine, I'd stayed in a hotel on a chestnut-tree-lined street, then continued the final eighty miles to Chernobyl by car. The very last few miles to the nuclear plant I was driven in a specially outfitted armored personnel carrier, because the radiation level had not yet been accurately determined.

Armored shields lifted slowly above the observation ports in the forward part of the olive-drab armored vehicle. Now I could see the road, a short length from the administration building to the stricken fourth reactor of the Chernobyl nuclear power plant.

With every pothole we hit in the road, the personnel carrier shook. So did the needle on the contraption that was fastened just behind my legs—it reminded me a bit of the meter in a taxicab—the Geiger counter.

For the first several dozen yards the background radiation wasn't very high. Suddenly, as we passed a hole in one of the plant's structures, the needle hit the top of the scale and stuck there; the radiation level right under our very wheels was really high. The driver wasn't going to dally. He stepped on the gas and we tore away.

But other people were already here—on foot—on the grounds, behind the walls of Reactor No. 4, in spots that were far more dangerous than where we had driven for just a moment. Firemen were dragging heavy fire hoses, hooking them to hydrants, directing the water at the blazing roof, climbing fire ladders, scouting the premises closely to determine whether people could venture into them. They were pressing forward with but a single goal in mind, driven by a single thought: to put out the fire as quickly as possible.

Meanwhile, just a few feet away, through the holes in the concrete made by the explosion, the damaged reactor leaked its lethal radiation. The monstrous temperature had melted the graphite, and now shards of protective cladding (a metal coating bonded onto another metal) were raining down on the workers as the nuclear fuel spewed its invisible death.

The fire alarm had first sounded in the middle of the night, at 1:23 A.M. The firefighters spent hours at the reactor, refusing to leave until they had completed their job. Many of them, burned by the fire or radiation or both, had had to be led outside or carried directly from the raging fire on the roof to waiting ambulances. Their comrades returned to the scene to finish the work.

The unique documents I will be quoting below are stories told from hospital beds by some of the twenty-eight people who were among the first to come face-to-face with the blaze in the wee hours of April 26. They were young people, just kids really, yet they were determined people who knew exactly what they were up against.

Had these young men not extinguished the fire as quickly as they did, it might have spread to one or more of the reactors nearby. I shudder to think about the possible consequences. They did everything humanly possible and saved many of us who lived far away from the Chernobyl nuclear plant.

The Ivan Shavrei Story

"I was born on January 3, 1956. My family's originally from Byelorussia. I work as a firefighter in the fire department at the Chernobyl Nuclear Power Plant.

"At the time the accident occurred, I was on duty in the department next to the control room along with Legun, the substitute dispatcher, and Nichiporenko, the duty officer who was about to take over. The three of us were standing and chatting, when suddenly we heard an explosion. The alarm went off and we drove to the reactor.

"Aleksandr Petrovsky and I climbed 200 feet of the ladder onto the roof of the control room. Some of the guys from Fire Company No. 6 had beaten us to it and they were already in bad shape. We helped them onto the extension ladder, but to get to the ground they still had to climb down that 200 feet.

"We headed toward the fire, where the heat seemed to be the most intense. We remained until we had put out the fire on the roof. Only then did we climb down. We were met by ambulances. Like the other men, we were in terrible shape.

"The night sky glowed from time to time with periodic flashes from the roof. Water was gushing from holes and openings in the reactor. Ambulances were everywhere. Everyone was exhausted, covered with grime, and badly burned. I still see ambulances, with red crosses on the roofs, picking up people and rushing them away from the reactor."

Vladimir Prischepa's Story

"On the twenty-sixth of April I was on duty at Reactor No. 4. The day shift had gone without incident, but after my rest period I was also scheduled to be on duty that night. I watched TV for a while and then I lay down for a while. Suddenly I heard the alarm. I pulled on my clothes and jumped into the truck. That's when I saw the flames in Reactor No. 4.

"The chief of the watch, Lieutenant Vladimir Pravik, got into the truck and radioed a Code 3, which is the most intense, dangerous kind of fire. That meant that all of the fire engines of the Kiev Administrative Region were obliged to come to our assistance.

"Obviously, a lot of them had come a long distance, which meant that we were among the first to get to the reactor. We had to take the brunt of the main impact. By the time we arrived, there wasn't any room for our fire engine; our buddies had already taken up all the spots adjacent to the reactor. I shouted to the driver to get closer. We finally found a special hookup for the water.

"I climbed onto the roof to scout out the situation. That's when I saw that the roof beams were in trouble. Some of them had begun to collapse. Flames were everywhere. I went back and saw Major Leonid Telyatnikov near the ladder, so I reported the situation to him. He told me to get up to the roof of the control room. Leonid Shavrei and I fought the fire there until morning, by which time I was in a pretty bad way. We washed up and I went to the doctor. That's about all I can tell you."

In a hospital ward everything is stark and white. An IV bottle is dripping into a tube; night nurses in white move here and there. And through a fine needle dangling from a tube, a stranger's blood is becoming your own.

Your own blood, meanwhile, is no longer yours; doctors replace it with increasing frequency. I am so moved I cannot bring myself to ask the young men from Chernobyl and Pripyat what they make of it all.

I'm holding another document in my hands, this one stamped with the official title, "Explanatory Report." In it Private Andrei Polovinkin tells the story not of his own heroic actions but of the bravery of his buddies. Toward the end of the affidavit Polovinkin succumbs to exhaustion and his handwriting trails off.

Private Andrei Polovinkin's Statement

"It took us three minutes to get to the site of the accident. We put our fire truck in place and started getting ready to put out the fire. I climbed up to the reactor's roof twice to relay the fire chief's orders.

"I want to applaud the bravery of Lieutenant Pravik personally. He knew he was subjecting himself to severe radiation injuries, yet he still went into that inferno and checked out every last detail. I also want to mention the courage of Ivan Shavrei, Leonid Shavrei, Aleksandr Petrovsky, and Bulava. I'm sure others did fine work as well in the effort to put out the fire, which went on long after I was carted off to the hospital."

It is apparent that the firemen knew perfectly well what they were getting themselves into. They had been trained for just such an eventuality; they knew what it was they were beating back. If it hadn't been for their exacting and selfless work, the danger zone might have been much greater than just eighteen miles.

Sergeant Aleksandr Petrovsky's Report

"Ivan Shavrei and I were instructed to climb the fire escapes up to the roof. We were there for fifteen or twenty minutes and did what we had to do to put the fire out. Then we came down; we couldn't have stayed there any longer. Afterward an ambulance picked us up. That was all."

As simple as that?

Commander Ivan Bugrimenko's Report

"In a situation like this, no one gives himself any slack. On the contrary, everyone showed a great deal of organization, unity of purpose, and capacity to make his own decisions. Even when those decisions are chancy, they're the only decisions that can be made in the particular situation. Everyone understood what he was getting into. Everything that was necessary for us to do we did with integrity.[22]

On the last page of the notebook that I filled on my first day in Chernobyl there was a list of names. It was dictated to me by the men who were carrying on the watch in the special zone. They asked that I name in my book the six of their comrades who lost their lives to the fire and the radiation:

Sergeant Nikolai Vashchuk
Lieutenant Viktor Kibenko
Lieutenant Vladimir Pravik
Master Sergeant Nikolai Titenko
Sergeant Vladimir Tishchuru

At the hospital I was struck again by the white, white ward, the dripping IV bottles, and the dedicated night nurses. Many of the people who followed the firefighters after that first night also ended up in hospital beds here, in Moscow, and in Kiev.

Not everyone whom I saw at the nuclear power plant was in critical condition. But even the doctors, specialists who had seen a lot in their day, were upset when they spoke of some of the others who were.

Every possible assistance in modern medicine, including bone marrow and donor blood, was given to help save the lives of these men. Indeed, we were fortunate that the painful list of firefighters who lost their lives was small: six the first night, and four more later on.

I moved around the site by personnel carrier. I went into the main structure with the chief of the plant's militarized fire department, Major Vladimir Mayevsky, who replaced Leonid Telyatnikov. Even blindfolded, Mayevsky could find his way to any point of the building's labyrinth of ducts and passageways.

It goes without saying that under the circumstances the strictest monitoring was essential. The job of the firefighters afterwards was complicated by the fact that the alarm system had stopped working, partly because of the damage to the lines and partly from the unusual ionization of the air. For that reason it became necessary to make visual checks of all the rooms and compartments of the huge structure.

Of course, you can't equate the firefighters of Chernobyl as you might the firemen back home. Everyone realizes how much more life threatening were the jobs the Chernobyl firefighters undertook. For example, they unhesitatingly led the operation that others took up only later—and even then with a lot of trepidation: team after team pumping contaminated water out of the pool that had formed under the crippled reactor, finally turning the valves, emptying the stationary pumps, drying up the pool, and averting the danger of a reaction between the reactor's white-hot elements and the water.

But one might ask, what's so terrible about dragging some hoses, dropping them into a pool, and turning on the pumps? The answer is that the water—and the premises around the reactor at that point—carried such extreme radiation that even in protective clothing people weren't allowed to work for more than a few minutes. And those few minutes could be lethal.

The greatest danger of all was the pool of water. Suspended over it, the reactor remained incandescent. If the hot fuel had come into contact with the water, there would have been an explosion even greater than the first, a detonation so great it would have shattered the sky with terrible violence as the structure burst at the seams.

But the firefighters triumphed, proving again that their worth was beyond measure.

What Happened?

What happened at Reactor No. 4 during the early morning hours of April 26 comes to life in the tales of the firefighters. But still, what caused the fire? What were the roots of these dramatic events?

Strange as it may seem, one of the roots of the accident was psychological. The people who work in a nuclear power plant know how very different the job feels from, say, work at a power plant that runs on coal. At an atomic reactor there is only silence. It's not like a coal stove. No one has to be concerned constantly about restoking the coal or about the coal's quality. At an atomic reactor the most anyone has to do is pay close attention to the readings on dials of a lot of equipment. It's the sort of situation that tends to allow a disorganized person to become lax.

Laxity, in other words, isn't a problem only at Chernobyl or at reactors elsewhere in the USSR; it's an important consideration at every nuclear power plant in the world today, including those in densely populated Europe.

The training of workers for nuclear power plants requires special attention and responsibility. Now, after the events at Chernobyl, plans are being made to increase the number of trainees and to give workers-to-be greater know-how. Special attention will also be given to preparing the workers at nuclear plants to make quick, informed decisions in extreme situations. The psychological preparedness of those who service nuclear power plants has to be reliable to the utmost degree possible.

It turned out that at Reactor No. 4 the workers had gotten away with a large number of gross violations of the regulations. The reactor was first put into operation in December 1983. From that time until the accident, its operation was considered perfectly satisfactory. So much so, in fact, that a certain amount of complacency may have developed. And that complacency, in turn, could indirectly have led to the irresponsibility and lack of discipline that resulted in the tragic consequences.

Here is the sequence of events. Reactor No. 4 was scheduled to have been shut down for repairs after two years of operation. But the power-plant management had also scheduled one of the turbogenerators for tests before the temporary shutdown was to begin. Unfortunately, the quality of the test protocol was poor, and certain essential safety measures weren't provided for.

The emergency cooling system was shut off a few hours before the accident—more precisely, at 2 P.M. on April 25. The people who were supposed to be doing the experiments were eager to get the procedure under way, but removal of the reactor from service in compliance with scheduling developed at Kievenergo was nevertheless delayed. Unfortunately the reactor remained in operation until the very last second—that is, until 1:23 A.M. on the morning of the twenty-sixth—**without a working emergency cooling system.**

Since the test protocol was not in accordance with the guidelines of either the representatives of the reactor's chief designer or the plant's main designer, or those of the nuclear safety board that was permanently stationed there, many of these specialists were at a loss during the first days to explain what happened. They didn't have the facts, and they couldn't have guessed at violations as outrageous as the ones that actually occurred.

There's a special term used in modern technology to guard against the possibility of human error: *idiot-proofing*. This means the creation of systems that guard themselves against improper use. It would appear that multiple backup systems and supermodern techniques and technologies would guard against accidents at a nuclear power plant. But the builders of the Chernobyl reactor—which was state of the art and in many respects superior to many other reactors of its kind—never considered idiot-proofing it. As a result, a colossally long, persistent chain of infractions of the rules ended suddenly, for everyone concerned—builders and experimenters alike—in an explosion.

Is the price of progress in energy too high if it means the

risk of nuclear accidents, with the attendant human casualties and contamination of the environment? It's difficult to come to any definitive conclusions just yet. It might seem simple and logical not to utilize power plants with such volatile fuel. But using that logic, shouldn't we refuse to manufacture chemicals as well? For just one instance, in 1947 in Texas City, Texas, there was a huge ammonium nitrate explosion in which 576 people died and another 2,000 were injured.

In 1979, not far from Toronto, Ontario, in Canada, there was a train wreck involving a train carrying gasoline, petroleum products, and chlorine. 250,000 people had to be evacuated from the surrounding area to escape the toxic fumes. But even a catastrophe as terrible as that one didn't put an end to Canada's use of its railroads.

Is ocean travel humdrum and safe? Or space exploration? Hardly. But too many genies would have to be stuffed back in their bottles if we began following the dictates of the logic that steers clear of anything that tempts fate or carries a danger signal.

Accidents related to technology are forcing scientists to seek greater safeguards.

The principal causes of technology-related accidents are shortcomings in the interaction between men and machines. What's more, the more complicated and more powerful the technology, the more expensive those shortcomings become in terms of human costs.

The solution lies not in rejecting technological progress, but in insisting on establishing a kind of balance between a human and machine that automatically offers each some gain—that is, a balance in which the machine won't allow the human to make the mistake, and the human will be able to override any malfunction on the part of the machine. Unfortunately, that optimal sort of situation has yet to be achieved—and I'm not just referring to atomic energy.

2

PRIPYAT AND CHERNOBYL AFTER THE ACCIDENT:
The First Days

Before going any further I would like to define more clearly certain of the circumstances surrounding the events under discussion, for instance, the geography.

In a way, the entire Chernobyl affair can be described in the name Chernobyl itself. The nuclear plant is actually more than eleven miles from the cozy little Ukrainian town and district center (population, 14,000) after which it is named. Thanks to its many green parks and gardens, the town of Chernobyl looks more like a village, albeit a rather large and well-to-do one.

Much nearer to the power plant is Pripyat, a modern city built to support it. The inhabitants of Pripyat are for the most part those who work at the power plant and their families. The city is 2.2 square miles in area and has a population of 45,000. It has eleven main streets totaling 7.4 miles. It has three main banks, ten restaurants, bars and cafes, an arts center, a movie theater, a dance hall, and twenty-three apartment buildings and dormitories.

When the Chernobyl accident was first announced and the government began to call up forces from every corner of the Kiev Administrative Region, it was actually to the city of Pripyat that they came. The firefighters and the specialists tested the city for radiation; after all, the catastrophe hadn't involved the town itself. If it had, what would have happened to the town's residents? No one really knows.

In telling how the firefighting was organized and what was being set up in Kiev to ensure the safety of the people in the area, I may have to repeat myself in order to relate the extensive and complex efforts that were undertaken during the terrible early morning hours of April 26.

■ ■ ■

The clock pointed to 1:23. At exactly that moment, the fire department's man on duty heard a deafening roar.

Lieutenant Pravik, the chief duty officer, automatically took note of the time and sounded the alarm. The next thing the men knew, the howl of the siren was filling their quarters. But even without it the firefighters realized they were needed. Already they were suiting up and running toward the trucks.

Immediately the dispatcher was in contact with the Pripyat fire department and then with the central fire switchboard in Kiev. The firefighters followed a Code 3, the dispatch used for the most extreme emergencies and requiring that all reserve and off-duty personnel get ready to respond.

In Kiev, the deputy chief of the Ukrainian Fire Administration, Lieutenant Colonel Ivan Kotsyura, and the chiefs of the subdepartments headed out immediately. The situation at the power plant was going to be extremely difficult to handle: a fire was blazing on the roof of the engine room on Reactor No. 4.

The first assignment was clear enough: put out the fire. It was a job that had to be done at great heights. And even for high-altitude work, this was hardly your ordinary fire. Because of the infernal heat, the asphalt on the roof was melting. Every step the men took to advance to the fire was unbelievably difficult. With each minute their boots, loaded with tar sticking to them, felt heavier and heavier.

Department head Major Leonid Telyatnikov led the attempt to put out the fire, scorning the radiation danger and battling the flames until he and his men stopped the threat of its spreading. That was the first priority since Reactors No. 1, 2, and 3 were frighteningly close by.

The police, too, performed superbly. First, they had to close the entrance to the city to all traffic not directly involved with the plant emergency or helping the victims. Second, they had to keep strict order in town; in situations like this nothing is worse than panic. Finally, they had to keep all nonessential vehicles away from the power plant.

By 4 A.M. the first police from the neighboring district of Polessk began arriving in Pripyat with the offer of additional help. After that, police started arriving from Chernobyl and Ivanovsk. All of the police forces were combined to address the jobs of organizing the various checkpoints, roadblocks, cordons, and in-town point duty.

The men on checkpoint duty were in a special structure just steps from the burning reactor, the actual scene of the accident. That was where it was most dangerous and where radiation levels were highest. Yet that was exactly where a stream of special-purpose vehicles was heading at top speed, and someone had to regulate the traffic. The police from Pripyat who were assigned the job on the first day worked ten- and twelve-hour shifts. They expended a lot of energy, but they brought order to the roads until the fire was out.

At the crack of dawn, scientists, engineers, and technicians boarded helicopters and began making reconnaissance flights over the plant to examine Unit No. 4 at close range, to determine the extent of the damage and measure the amount of radiation the reactor had released into the air.

What sort of danger did they face? Unquestionably it was great. But only by performing this work could they answer with any precision the questions that had to be answered before any further steps could be taken. They exposed themselves to this hazard for the sake of those people still sleeping in Pripyat, unsuspecting of the danger near them.

Soon the helicopters started taking cargoes on board, too— lead shot, sandbags, bags full of other special powders. These were dropped from the air in an attempt to plug up the crater that the explosion had blown in the reactor; it seemed the best way to stem the radiation-contaminated exhausts the crater was spewing out. The pilots descended to low altitudes so that the drops could be made with the greatest possible accuracy. It was a difficult maneuver at that point since the fire had warped the roof and demolished the floor beams, and it was melting a fixture that was sticking up dangerously out of the hole.

What started that morning continued methodically, hour after hour, day after day, as the MI-8 helicopters hovered overhead in this highly intricate mission until the levels of radiation began to diminish.

At Reactor No. 4 the work was strenuous and the radiation still very high—although, as it turned out, not universally so. Perhaps because of the helicopters, here and there the radiation levels dropped; a map of radiation levels would have presented a picture resembling "pockmarks" left on an ill person's face. Some places were thick with radiation; others were nearly devoid of it. But in the beginning, this wasn't known.

However, the radiation situation in Pripyat was unclear. Still, the authorities began taking protective measures around eight o'clock, as soon as the town began waking up.

Doctors started making the rounds of the town. As a preventive measure they got hold of every available medication containing iodine. This was needed to keep the radioactive isotopes of iodine, which are the typical results of an accident like the one at the Chernobyl plant, from taking over in the body. The importance of this measure cannot be overestimated; by the end of the day the doctors had finished their efforts to protect the populace with stable iodine. Unfortunately, there has not always been such success in nuclear emergencies. Soviet physicians had learned much from the most recent nuclear accident, the one at Three Mile Island, where there were four full days before any fresh iodine-containing medications had been distributed.

At Chernobyl, what was it like the morning after? Klavdiya Radul, who lives in Pripyat, remembers.

The Klavdiya Radul Story

"We got up early—seven o'clock. I was rushing around trying to get Vitalik, my son, off to school, while I was in a hurry to get to the grocery. I wanted to get some green vegetables; my family likes them, but I especially needed the vitamins because I was expecting a child in another month. My husband was the only one in the house who was asleep; he'd just gotten in from fishing.

"When I arrived at the market, it seemed to be closed. Obviously something had happened. And then I was told there'd been some kind of accident over at the plant. The news hit me like a bolt.

"I rushed over to the school to get my boy. The school was locked, and they weren't letting the children out. They tried to calm me down as best they could. They said that the kids would be safe there. And then over the radio they told us—the doctors told us—what we should do next.

"They explained that it would be best not to allow the children outside, and that it would be a good idea if we, the grownups, could stay indoors, too. My son finally got home after lunch, and from then on we didn't go anywhere.

"By the next day, Sunday morning, they came knocking on the door and ordered us to get ready to evacuate and, if we could, to take along enough food for two days.

"During the course of the day there was another radio communiqué. They said that by two in the afternoon buses would be coming to pick us up. They asked us not to bring anything extra along. Of course, we were all pretty upset, and we didn't understand a lot of what was going on. But more than anything else, I was worried about whether I should bring swaddling clothes, just in case I suddenly gave birth on the way. And I was worried about Vitalik, too, whether he'd be O.K. without school, and so on. You see, no one really knew how long we'd be gone."

Evacuation: that terrible word we all knew and associated only with World War II. But *here!*—here, on this tranquil day, under this clear, blue sky! Evacuation: a complicated move that has to be carried out with tact and understanding on the one hand, and with real dispatch on the other.

Between the police and the town officials, the evacuation was carried out admirably. The entire city of Pripyat was divided into five sectors, each comprising one of the town's five residential neighborhoods. Five respective evacuation groups were set up, accordingly.

On the twenty-sixth the Ukrainian Republic's deputy minister of the interior, Gennadi Berdov, arrived in Pripyat. Police Major General Aleksandr Borovik arrived on the twenty-seventh. Neither returned to Kiev unti May 4, by which time all of the most intricate operations had been carried out.

The principal burden of the evacuation depended mostly upon the divisional inspectors of the city of Pripyat. The actual speed and efficiency of the evacuation depended on them. All night and half of the next day the lists of the town's residents were drawn up. Evacuation workers were assigned equal numbers of homes and housing complexes (there were seven hundred of the latter in all), and the transport that would be needed was tallied up. Each bus was assigned a sector with an exact route and schedule.

Borovik's Story

"The evacuation was announced for 2 P.M. At 1:30 a worker appeared at the entrance to each apartment building. This person then went through all the apartments and warned the people by reiterating what they should already have heard on the radio. Collection points were set up so as to avoid commotion and panic. And we achieved the desired effect."

The results speak for themselves: in the course of less than three hours practically the entire population of the town was evacuated, in a stream of 1,100 buses that stretched along the highway for more than twelve miles—amazingly, without traffic jams.

A handful of people who for one reason or another weren't evacuated with the other residents of their building gathered at the police station. They were quickly dispatched to the major collection points and put on the first available bus.

Even people who had gone fishing or hunting in the nearby woods before dawn were tracked down.

But police did tell me a sad story about two old women who hid themselves far away and so well that they couldn't be found even after the entire locale was combed; in fact, it wasn't until May 28 that the two women finally emerged from their hiding place—and had to go straight to the hospital. One was eighty-five, and the other seventy-four. At their age it was too painful to tear themselves away from their lifelong belongings. And who could reproach them? Who could scold them for it? One could only wish them health and peace in their old age.

The city was empty. But the homes, the shops, and the institutions couldn't remain wide open and unguarded. Immediately following the evacuation the security service sprang into action, and all the personal property of the town's 45,000 residents was put under the round-the-clock guard. The only vehicles rolling down the streets of the desolate town were special patrols. Meanwhile, in the other villages, temporary shelters awaited the evacuees until new places of residence were determined.

Unfortunately that wasn't the entire extent of the evacuation, as the scientists had decided to evacuate everyone within a radius of eighteen miles. Inside the defined circle, the only people who remained behind were those who were actually addressing the aftereffects of the accident and those who worked at the three other reactor units, which had since been shut down. A registration service and directory were organized for people who'd gotten lost.

The moment the crisis began, the emergency alarm sounded at the Ukrainian Ministry of Health, and from then on the lights burned through the night on every floor. Says the head of the Central Medical Preventive and Therapeutic Assistance Administration, Kozlyuk: "The Ministry's duty officer woke me up with a phone call before dawn. I don't live too far from the Ministry, so I made my way there quickly. The information received gave me no choice but to make some quick decisions."

Within minutes ambulances were racing toward Chernobyl from every subdivision of Kiev itself and from every district hospital in the Kiev Region. In a few hours, enough medical personnel had gathered in the administrative districts surrounding the nuclear power plant to conduct screening examinations of the people who had been near the plant and to care for them.

There were many people in need of treatment. Some of those who had been helping to put out the fire in Reactor No. 4 were too ill to describe what finally happened. Actually they were carried out by medical workers.

The following is testimony of eyewitnesses and of the doctors who were among the first to arrive on the scene. Special Medical Unit No. 126 was the one that found itself nearest to the actual scene of the tragedy. Professor Angelina Guskova, a department deputy director at the Moscow Clinic, where the people who had been most seriously hurt and whose radiation sickness was considered ultracritical were later operated on, recalls that all the medical people, and particularly the specialists from 126, did an extraordinary job. Out of a large number of people they were able to identify the patients who were the most exhausted or burned or suffering from smoke inhalation—in other words, the patients who were most seriously in need of treatment. Imagine what it was like there after an explosion and fire:

"The doctors did everything necessary to transfer the seriously ill to Kiev and Moscow immediately with as little loss as possible. But during the first, most difficult days, they also did thousands of analyses and examinations right on site, in the high-radiation zone."

It was from this group that the first 100 patients were selected for transfer in three planes, under extreme-emergency priority. The nation's best medical professors, specialists with worldwide reputations, received referrals from the local physicians, the latter becoming the first doctors in the world to encounter such cases.

Tatyana Benadysenko, a Surgeon with Clinic No. 126

"Camp Fairy Tale, a summer camp for school kids, was turned into an infirmary. Here the medical personnel could administer care and follow the progress of the nuclear plant workers.

"All the medical people, from the nurses to the teaching staff, worked nonstop around the clock. To find a suffering victim, to carry him out, to get him to the casualty ward, and then to go back and start all over again with the next victim—that's what my colleagues did during the terrible, dark morning of the twenty-sixth and the following day. They surveyed the scene of the accident for victims, they provided first aid where necessary, and they got the people who needed medical care over to the infirmary.

"It seemed endless; all you could see were sick people in need of help who kept coming in an uninterrupted stream. Every ward in the treatment division became an intensive care unit. Decontamination took up a huge amount of time and energy. The staff provided everything necessary, organized a standardized radiation testing procedure, and administered preventive iodine.

"And then came the first real blow: one of the patients died. We knew that a person as sick as he was was never going to make it; yet, even so . . . we felt so helpless!

"But there remained dozens of other sick people whose lives we still had to fight to save."

Forgetting an experience like that is not a simple matter. And one of the reminders is the pine trees. Once there were numerous pine trees near the plant; then right before your eyes many of them yellowed and died. I've been told that pine trees are especially vulnerable to radiation.

Many of the first groups of people with burns and radiation sickness ended up a long way from the reactor. The lucky ones were those who simply reached the time limit that had been imposed on workers in the accident zone, and then transferred out.

The remainder were the most badly in need of treatment. The strong radiation during the first few days had affected the medical personnel from Pripyat. None of them would have expected to become a patient himself.

Thus a ticket for a tour of Central Asia in May lay unused on a nighttable in the Pripyat apartment of operating room nurse Liliya Bulyavichene.

So it was that Dr. Aleksandr Yakimchuk, who carried a patient to the Polessk hospital on April 28, suddenly found himself being hospitalized for radiation sickness. He chalked it up to a mistake accountable to the stress of work. He asked the driver of his ambulance to wait and pick him up. Surely, he'd be pronounced fine by his colleagues in the morning; surely, he couldn't have radiation sickness.

Though trouble never comes at a good time, the accident didn't catch the doctors unprepared. Here's how some of the doctors at Clinic No. 126 spent the night of April 25–26.

Valentin Belokon, Emergency Room Physician

"I was on call all night—one emergency after another. But for an E.R. physician, I guess that's par for the course. When I returned to the hospital, just after 2 A.M., I hadn't even stepped inside the door when the dispatcher shouted to me, 'Get over to the nuclear plant right away—there's a fire over there! Sasha Skachok [the paramedic] has already left.'

"I raced over and found the firemen already there. I arranged the three ambulances where everyone could see them. We were 100 meters from the reactor.

"The first people we examined were the firefighters. Suddenly, there was so much to do that our three drivers, Gumarov, Vinokur, and Yurchenko, were working nonstop driving back and forth, plant to hospital, hospital to plant. At about five o'clock I noticed a sort of metallic taste in my mouth. Soon after I began developing a headache and nausea. I recognized the symptoms of radiation sickness and requested permission to leave. They replaced me with Galina Navoichik."

Anatoli Vinokur, Ambulance Driver

"As soon as the first alarm sounded, Skachok the paramedic and I drove to the nuclear plant together with the firemen. The minute we arrived they brought a man to us with burns all over his body. I later found out that his name was Aleksandr Shashenok, and that he was a unit operator at the power plant.

"We drove to the hospital as fast as we could. Then I drove back six more times. They kept checking the ambulance for radiation. The needle, which indicates the radiation level, leaned way over to one side. It meant that the radiation danger was very great. But we simply had to rescue the victims.

"I didn't get home until morning. My wife got scared because I took off my clothes at the door and left them outside. And that afternoon I was back at work again."

Vladimir Pecheritsa, Deputy Chief Resident at Clinic No. 126

"Practically everyone who was needed was rounded up by 3 A.M., while the fire was still raging over the plant. My wife and I—she's a doctor, too—tried to slip out of the house quietly so as not to wake our sons. But as it turned out they woke up anyway and were pretty upset, especially the young one.

"The department heads over at the clinic, Nuriakhmedov, Ben, and Maltseva, made several decisions right away: they washed, dressed the wounds, and did the first blood transfusions on the patients arriving from the plant. They reassigned the ones who were already in the clinic, carried in and set up more beds, and made up more solutions. By the evening of the twenty-sixth the first group of victims was sent by special train to hospitals in Moscow."

Liliya Bulyavichene, Operating Room Nurse

"A telephone call woke me up. Even before they told me, I knew from their tone of voice that the situation was bad. By the time I arrived, Sasha Shashenok was already on a resuscitator. I didn't recognize him though we live in the same building."

During these first days the medical personnel who were most worried were those who had loved ones working over at the plant. Like everyone else, nurse Lyuda Shashenok was awakened by the alarm. Because of it she was able to spend her husband's final hours with him.

Once the evacuation of Pripyat had begun, the medical personnel were among the last to leave, remaining on call after all of the town's residents had left. As long as the accident victims kept arriving at the clinic, the medical people continued to look after them, even doing the laundry and cooking the food.

For reasons of hygiene, the kitchen and the boiler room were closed down; the medical staff started bringing in food from home to feed everyone in the clinic. They even dragged over somebody's washing machine.

The situation didn't ease up until sometime toward the end of the day on April 28, when a large brigade of doctors and lab technicians arrived from Moscow.

▪ ▪ ▪

Vladimir Pecheritsa isn't likely ever to forget 48 River Street, Volodarka Village, in the Borodyansky Administrative District—the home of people he barely knew. But these people took in his wife and sons as if they were their own. He spent a few precious moments there before returning to the clinic.

It was later on, after the crisis was over, that Pecheritsa's wife went to Dzerzhinsky, where she is district physician. And it was later on that his elder son went back to school to finish out the year. But it was in Volodarka Village that they spent the most difficult days. A large number of medical people, busy during the first days of the emergency, had to spend time to search for their families.

All of the medical people knew what they were getting into. Nevertheless, out of a sense of duty, they went—the doctors, the nurses, and the auxiliary personnel. Just the way the fire-fighters and the nuclear power engineers who were working alongside them went: they too understood the danger they faced.

One story making the rounds best explained the value of their sacrifice. A worker who had been on the final shift [sic. and obviously ran away] sent a telegram from a distant city asking whether he might be of help.

Nobody bothered answering him.

Reactor Number Four at the Chernobyl nuclear plant from 18 hours after the accident through the stages of containment. Finally, the entire reactor was entombed in concrete. Workers, using automated equipment, tunneled under the damaged reactor. Cement was poured under it. A steel structure was fabricated, on which concrete was used to create a total "sarcophagus," which prevents any further radiation leaks. The undamaged have been sealed off from Number Four.

The photographs following show the containment process in chronological sequence.

PHOTOGRAPHS WERE TAKEN BY THE FOLLOWING RUSSIAN
PHOTOGRAPHERS:

V. Zufarov
A. Poddubny
A. Bormotov
V. Falin
B. Repik
A. Malakhovsky
V. Samokhotsky
V. Solovyov
K. Dudchenko
M. Chernichkin
A. Madolenko
Yuri Inyakina
Yu. Mosenzhnika

THE DAMAGED REACTOR NUMBER 4 LEAKING RADIATION.
UNSEEN, A POOL OF RADIOACTIVE WATER.

A HELICOPTER INVOLVED IN DUST SUPPRESSION ON THE
ROOFS OF REACTORS #3 AND #4

CHERNOBYL. PUTTING UP THE LAST PART OF THE PROTECTIVE
WALL DIVIDING UNIT #3 AND #4

A TRESTLE "BRIDGE" FOR TRANSFERRING CEMENT TO BUILD
THE CONTAINMENT WALL

CONSTRUCTING PART OF THE "SARCOPHAGUS" OVER UNIT #4

IN PROCESS: THE FRAMEWORK FOR THE PROTECTIVE WALL
FOR THE UNIT #4

ANOTHER MEETING OF THE GOVERNMENT COMMISSION

THE "SARCOPHAGUS" OVER UNIT #4. THE VIEW IS FROM THE
SIDE OF THE WALL.

THE SITE WHERE THE METAL STRUCTURAL ELEMENTS ARE
ASSEMBLED FOR THE WALLING IN OF REACTOR #4

THE BLIMP CARRIES RADIATION MONITORING EQUIPMENT.
BELOW, PRELIMINARY WORK HAS BEGUN TO SEAL UNIT #4.

BUILDING UNIT #4'S CONTAINMENT WALL.

THE FIRST USE OF CONCRETE ON THE DAMAGED ROOF OF
UNIT #4

WORK DURING THE FIRST STAGES OF CLEARING DEBRIS.

TESTING RADIATION LEVELS

WORK ON THE "SARCOPHAGUS" CONTINUED DAY AND NIGHT.

ENTOMBMENT NEARS COMPLETION. CONCRETE WAS POURED
UNDER #4 AS WELL.

ASSEMBLING AND PREFABRICATING SECTIONS TO BE USED TO
HOLD CEMENT IN THE UNIT #4 CONTAINMENT STRUCTURE

WORK OF REACTOR #4 WAS CONTINUOUS UNTIL IT WAS
COMPLETELY SEALED OFF.

3

RADIATION:
Panic Is as Dangerous as Neglect

The threat of radiation is at once dangerous and terrifying. It is invisible and deadly. We know that even the youngest child will pull his hand away from a lighted match. He doesn't have to understand anything about fire to understand it is dangerous; he only has to know that fire can hurt. So too with radiation. Evolution over the millennia has developed in us an instinct for self-preservation. It has taught us to avoid harmful situations and to try to save our own lives when they're endangered.

Earthquakes, fires, floods, and avalanches—all these threaten human life. But in the brief history of the human race, it has become clear that there's no greater danger to humanity than man himself. The threat that our species presents to itself is not always as obvious as the flames of a fire.

But since the dawn of history, what frightens man more than anything else is the unknown.

Radiation? What is it exactly?

Radiation

It can't be seen, heard, or felt; when it comes to radiation, the five senses, which we depend on to warn us when danger is near, are powerless to help. In fact, when it comes to radiation, even knowledge doesn't help.

From the seventeenth century to the beginning of the present century, the great thinkers placed their trust in experience, submitted only to provable, observable, tangible fact. Careful observation and common sense are no longer sufficient. The average person accepts the laws of physics on faith: melting snow, a boiling kettle, a braking automobile—the classical laws of physics explain thousands of observable facts and realities. But as physicists, biologists, and chemists delve deeper into the properties of cells, molecules, and subatomic particles, the more hopeless become the attempts of the average person to comprehend the essence of matter.

Most people have to accept on faith information on subjects like radiation. And human psychology is such that when the information we receive is unsupported by our own sensory experience, it can easily give rise to a multitude of myths and exaggerations.

At the same time, and just as unacceptable as blind faith or misunderstanding, ignorance can lead to a scorn for danger. "Does the danger really exist?" people ask. The day after the Chernobyl accident occurred, the sky was as blue as the sky of the day before; the woods still rustled and the strawberries still ripened.

And so it was in Kiev and elsewhere: some people didn't acknowledge the seriousness of the danger, while other people blew it out of all proportion. People demanded facts, supporting information. They were anxious to know everything. Popular science periodicals, as well as serious books that had been gathering dust on library shelves, were now being grabbed by the insistent and the curious.

More than anything else, from Kiev to Moscow people wanted to know what substances the damaged reactor had expelled into the air. Because these questions were repeated so frequently, I believe it might be worthwhile discussing them at this point.

When they're working properly, nuclear reactors at electric power plants produce a very broad array of radioactive nuclides. Along with the production of various kinds of energy, these substances (which can be both solid and gaseous) undergo a variety of chemical transformations within the reactor. The accident at the Chernobyl reactor and the consequent thermal explosion led to a release of these solid and gaseous substances into the surroundings. The radioactive elements were no longer in the sealed atomic pile; they were fully exposed in the outside world.

Thousands of articles have been written about radioactive fallout, but too little has been said about alpha and beta particles, gamma rays and neutrons, about how certain of these rays of particles can't even penetrate cigarette paper or bathroom tissue, while others can penetrate a thick concrete wall. Unfortunately, all of these types of radiation were present in the vicinity of the accident at the Chernobyl plant. And they most definitely affected all living things.

Medical authorities divide the effects of irradiation into whether the exposure is external or internal. In external exposure the sources of the radiation are outside the body. Dealing with that should be easy enough: leave the danger zone and you leave the matter behind. Internal radiation concerns doctors much more: what happens when the radioactive substance is actually taken into the body?

The principal airborne product of the explosion at Chernobyl, iodine 131 has a half-life of eight days. It accumulates exclusively in the thyroid gland, an extremely important endocrine gland that manufactures the various hormones that regulate the body's metabolic intensity and rates of growth and development. Normally, the human body contains very little iodine, about 25 milligrams, with a concentration in the blood of only about one hundred-thousandth of a percent. But the thyroid tries to absorb all the iodine that enters the body until it becomes saturated. In a Chernobyl-type situation, the iodine the thyroid takes up can be radioactive. It should be obvious that concentrating all of that iodine into a single, rather small gland can lead to hormonal dysfunction. Such an accumulation is particularly dangerous in children, since hormones play a larger role in childhood development than in the adult. For this reason the doctors in Chernobyl paid special attention to the problem of iodine 131, especially in children.

During the first hours and days after the accident it was essential to supply the body with abundant amounts of nonradioactive iodine-containing substances, to feed the thyroid as much iodine as it could take. (This the doctors did, as I've described in an earlier chapter.) After this, the thyroid has no more room, so it can't absorb the radioactive iodine.

Having heard about this procedure, several people decided to medicate themselves. They bought tincture of iodine in their local drugstores—the antiseptic you use when you cut your finger—and they drank it. But using iodine more than ten days after a nuclear accident makes no sense. In the first place, if the iodine 131 has gotten into the system, it has already begun to work its damage and will continue to do so until it's either decomposed or eliminated from the body. At this point substitution isn't possible.

Moreover, if you're going to *drink* the iodine, you can't use the tincture but only special preparations. Tincture of iodine will burn the mucous membranes of the esophagus and stomach, and this can (and unfortunately in these cases *did*) lead to internal lesions.

But the problem of iodine 131 is always settled quickly; within days it is no longer dangerous. Its half-life, I repeat, is exceedingly short.

The question remains: if iodine 131 does enter the body, can it actually cause radiation sickness? In large doses it can cause extremely acute hormonal disturbances; in very large doses it can actually destroy the thyroid gland itself. However, it can't cause radiation sickness per se.

Current knowledge allows us to draw only the most general picture of the genetic consequences of irradiating the body. Parents who receive doses of radiation will increase the genetic variability of their offspring; this fact was first demonstrated long ago. There is also no doubt that the probability of genetic mutations is directly proportional to the radiation dose. Theoretically these mutations can be either advantageous or detrimental, but the probability of harmful mutations is incommensurately higher. These changes include:

a reduction in the life span
inclination to psychiatric disorders
lessened capacity to resist infection
a predisposition to developing certain malignancies

Curiously, though it has been established that irradiating the mother is more likely to affect a couple's prospective children than irradiating the father, nevertheless, irradiating the father is more likely to result in genetic mutation among the grand-children and subsequent generations.

Professor Yuri Grigoryev, at the USSR Institute of Biophysics, was head of a unique experiment to evaluate the effects of various doses of radiation on the body. As in a great deal of medical and biological research, the experimental subjects were dogs. During the course of several years, about two hundred fifty animals were subjected to nonstop, round-the-clock gamma irradiation. They were examined daily. In addition, every two months the researchers evaluated the condition of the chromosomal apparatus of the animals' bone-marrow cells, a variety of immunological and biochemical reactions, brain and spinal-cord function, and reactions to various stresses. After terminating the irradiation, the dogs were observed for the rest of their lives, as were their offspring: a period of more than sixteen years. The results showed that the frequency with which malignant tumors appeared didn't increase, the animals' reproductive capacity didn't change, and the life span of the experimental animals was, if anything, a bit greater than that of the controls.

Special investigations showed that it is possible to transfer these data to man—although it should be understood that this entails a certain margin of error, since the human life span is significantly longer than that of a dog; irradiating a dog for six years corresponds more or less to about twenty-five years in the case of a human being. The experiment was conducted to determine the effect of cosmic radiation on astronauts. The ambient radiation in space is greater than on earth, since on earth the atmosphere acts as a protective shield. Cosmic radiation is a constant influence in space flight. Moreover, astronauts can be exposed to additional irradiation from solar flares and prolonged flight through the earth's radiation belts. The radiation dose might be as high as 100 roentgens a year.

For the sake of comparison, let me point out that the maximum permissible dose for rescue workers at nuclear accidents is 25 roentgens, which gives the workers a rather large margin. Any worker who has received a dose of 25 roentgens, regardless of his function at the scene of the accident, is obliged to get out of the danger zone. A dose as high as 25 roentgens is considered the exception, and it can be said with certainty that *no one* gets more than 25 roentgens while at work.

All international commissions, committees, and agreements consider 25 roentgens within the realm of safety. People who have been exposed to that much radiation are allowed to return to work where they'll be exposed to radiation, with one proviso: they must not be exposed to more than a total of 50 additional roentgens during their lifetime.

Here an explanation is probably in order. The lifetime dose that the typical nuclear power plant worker receives during a twenty-five-year career averages between 19 and 25 roentgens. But people who have no connection to industrial reactors and who don't live anywhere near a nuclear plant also receive radiation. The earth's natural background radiation is rising. In the Soviet Union, as in the world's other industrially developed nations, the average dose a person picks up in a lifetime is approximately 25 to 28 roentgens. It never disappears; it simply adds up. This total amount is accumulated in the main from such sources as natural radionuclides in building materials and irradiation in the course of medical diagnostic procedures.*

But it's one thing to be in an X-ray room where brief pulses of carefully regulated radiation are being administered; it's quite another to spend time in a place where you're exposed to an extreme variety of radioactive sources, including all kinds of radiation, a large amount of various particulate and gaseous substances, and radioactive isotopes that penetrate the skin, accumulate in the body, and themselves become a continuing source of internal radiation.

---

*In recent years, a huge effort has been made to minimize the doses from medical X-rays and related procedures. In the 1950s, a patient undergoing gastrointestinal fluoroscopy or a chest X-ray would be receiving a dose of up to 1 roentgen; lower radiation didn't produce satisfactory test results. Today the technology has been improved, and the doses are accordingly lower; there is simply no need anymore to expose a person to so much radiation to achieve the same results. But even the radiation levels that were typical for the 1950s didn't produce negative after-effects.

There is a certain concept called the *effective dose*. If, let's say, a person has somehow been exposed to radiation for several years and has received an actual total of 1,000 roentgens, the so-called effective dose is considered to be between 200 and 300 roentgens; the body has been able to cope with all the rest, and there is a restoration of, or compensation for, lost functions. This has been shown experimentally in animals.

This restoration of function goes on at quite an active level. Take, for example, a case of acute radiation sickness: if a bit of the bone marrow is left undamaged by the ionizing radiation, it is capable of manufacturing fresh blood cells again. In animal experiments that were conducted to see how well an astronaut's body could stand up to exposure to solar flares, the researchers tried screening just a single bone at a time from the radiation. In one case the hip was studied. The animals survived significant doses of radiation and even coped with ones that were deliberately lethal.

In the opinion of Professor Grigoryev, there was no reason to expect acute symptoms of any sort in the wake of the accident at the Chernobyl plant. The main potential danger was associated with accumulating radioactive iodine in the thyroid during the first days after the accident. However, calculating the average doses, Grigoryev drew up a mathematical model that showed that a small number of cases of treatable cancers and benign tumors—from 40 to 320 for every million people—could show up at a later date.

Of course this mathematical model couldn't take every last factor into account, but in developing it, as in determining the radiation dose limits, a mass of allowances were included, where the human being was given the benefit of the doubt. Maximal caution had to be exercised. It was essential to check agricultural produce in the most painstaking fashion possible and to work out ways of safely farming contaminated plots. And there had to be a guarantee of utter safety before sending people back to contaminated areas.

Chernobyl has taught us many lessons.

Ionizing radiation can't be seen, it can't be heard, and it can't be felt—and average people aren't capable of a critical evaluation of its dangers. Only knowledge can make that evaluation possible: facts and figures from which rules can be drawn up and protective measures taken.

Today, with atomic energy in such wide use, it's necessary not only to increase the reliability of nuclear installations to the maximum degree possible, but unconditionally to think through the worst-case scenarios of every conceivable emergency.

Such work is currently going on, and what happened after the destruction of Unit No. 4 at the Chernobyl plant coincided in large measure with one of these scenarios—namely, the release of large amounts of radioactive iodine.

Carrying out radiation safety measures depends on the character of the accident, the location of the particular nuclear plant, and metereological conditions at the time of the accident. All of this presupposes a certain flexibility in the decision-making process. However the effectiveness of any measures will undoubtedly depend on the speed with which they can be instituted.

Local people have to know about the existence of plans in the event of an emergency, and there have to be clear and simple instructions for the first steps to be taken in the face of a radiation threat.

It would be great never to have to make use of such plans, but there's no getting around the importance of knowing what to do.

4

GROCERIES ON KIEV'S DINNER TABLES:
How They Are Tested

Aside from the wish to satisfy a "theoretical" hunger, a thirst for as much scientific information as possible, there are questions of a practical nature that concern people.

Advice and misinformation about what should and should not be done, about what was harmful and what was useful, were passed from person to person after the accident. Occasionally it took on an almost fantasy-like character. Often it was hard to disabuse people of their misapprehensions. For example, there was a lot of talk about the beneficial effects of alcoholic beverages on people who were living in the high-radiation zone. "Eyewitnesses" insisted that in Kiev, wine was being sold on every street corner, at very reduced prices to boot. Doctors and specialists who were approached to help clarify the matter only threw up their hands. In fact, alcohol does exercise a chemical effect on the body's organs: the nervous system (which includes the brain) and the liver. Radiation has a physical effect, on the cellular level. That is, alcohol and radiation have parallel but nonintersecting effects on the body. Occasionally they interact, but alcohol has no healing properties when it comes to radiation.

Certain firemen and workers at the nuclear plant who returned home after the terrible night of the fire tried to relax with a few shots of vodka after the monstrous tensions of the emergency work. According to their own testimony, and in the

55

reports of their doctors, a glass of alcohol not only didn't make them feel better, it immediately made them sick. Having gone to the doctor, such victims of radiation sickness were not able to describe very clearly how they actually felt as their brains were clouded by alcohol. In the face of the dangerous enemy called radiation, the brain works better sober than drunk.

More than anything else, health questions were connected with foodstuffs. For example, was the monitoring reliable? The strict monitoring of produce was set up immediately after the nuclear accident. All groceries delivered to the outdoor markets were tested, as were those sent to the state-run stores.

In Kiev some of the summer vegetable markets were closed down in order to ensure strict monitoring of the largest and most popular markets. Limitations were established on sales of home-prepared dairy products, vegetables, and mushrooms; forest-gathered wild berries were disallowed. Everything else was examined very strictly. For example, to monitor strawberries, the berries were mashed up in a jar and probed with a radiation dosimeter. Once in Kiev, I chanced to observe how one enterprising merchant tried to avoid the checkpoint for monitoring: he thrust his sackful of berries underneath the fence surrounding the market. The way the indignant shoppers drove that businessman out of the marketplace was quite a sight. Usually, the certificate of passage through the monitoring system lay there alongside the groceries themselves, and any shopper could demand to see it. Those who weren't satisfied with simply seeing the certificate could visit the inspection point and test their own purchases to convince themselves with their own eyes that the purchases were radiation-free.

At the Moscow markets all newly delivered produce was inspected. It happened on occasion that contaminated vegetables and berries were discovered. In order to stop the dosimeter's ringing, the rule was to thoroughly wash all items: the alarm indicating the presence of radiation usually wasn't from the items themselves but from the dust that had settled on them. Of course, it's always more wholesome to wash dust and dirt off fruits and vegetables, whether or not they're radioactive.

As far as milk and milk products were concerned, they were inspected at least twice—once on the farm and again at the bottling or processing plant. If the milk turned out to be contaminated with radioactive iodine, it was reprocessed. (Butter and cheese made from the reprocessed milk present no danger.)

The norms established for admissible iodine-131 content was ten times stricter than the allowable amounts established in Great Britain after the nuclear accident there, when radioactive isotopes of iodine entered the atmosphere.

Many people wanted to know whether the cows in the radiation zone presented a danger to people: couldn't they themselves become a source of radiation? In truth, if the radioactive fallout settled on the hides, then the cattle were radioactive. But wherever that happened it was sufficient to wash the cattle to remove the fallout, and this was done.

A more serious situation arises when cattle actually graze on contaminated grass, in which case the radioactive elements enter the milk. It is the latter situation that makes inspection so essential. This led to the reprocessing of shipments of contaminated milk. The amount of radioactive substances that a cow's body could absorb would not be so great as to allow a cow to become a radiation source. In addition, the beef from cattle that graze in the radioactive fallout zone is significantly less radioactive than the manure they leave behind. So the animals themselves don't present a danger. Chernobyl cattle were not slaughtered, although it's common knowledge that cattle exposed to very large amounts of radioactive contamination must be destroyed. For example, in Japan in 1954 more than 400 tons of fish that had been contaminated with radioactive substances were destroyed. It stands to reason that beef cattle that have been in a radiation zone can be used for food only so long as the traces of radioactivity don't exceed established safety levels.

The water question seriously worried everyone, not only the citizens of the Ukraine, but also scientists and people who customarily spend their summer vacation in the Crimea and other resorts on the Black Sea coast. In the first days after the accident along the Pripyat River they started building embankments to prevent contaminated water from entering the river. The Pripyat flows into the Kiev Reservoir and also into the Dnieper, the source of fresh water for a city of two million and a densely populated countryside around it. The fact that it didn't

rain in the period immediately following the nuclear accident
helped enormously by preventing that run-off water from flow-
ing over exposed areas and becoming contaminated. The situation was serious enough for urgent countermeasures to be
taken: it was necessary to create a reserve water supply. Within
a month a pumping station had been built to supply Kiev with
water from an alternative river, the Desna. In various of the
city's districts, fifty-eight artesian wells were drilled, ranging
in depths from 160 to 330 meters. Work proceeded at an
impressive pace considering Kiev's rocky ground. Additional
wells were drilled at all of Kiev's major dairy plants and
bakeries. The only water they used came from these artesian
wells.

The most difficult jobs were those associated with underground streams in the region of the nuclear plant itself. They
had to be prevented from carrying radioactive wastes into the
Pripyat River. For this a network of holes was enclosed, and the
direction of underground rivers and streams was altered so that
they circumvented the nuclear plant.

Kiev never switched to artesian well water; as before, the
city obtained most of its drinking water from the Dnieper.
Measurements of the radiation showed that the water presented no danger. Water samples were taken hourly, at exactly
the same time and at exactly the same spots, as a rule where the
river flows fastest throughout its entire course: from the area
nearest the nuclear plant to the city itself. Water was sampled
on site, in floating laboratories, as well as at institutes in Kiev.

When summer came, many people who usually take trips
to the Black Sea wouldn't go. Rumor and exaggeration of the
danger spread. Nobody wants to spend a vacation concerned
about radiation danger. That, after all, is human nature: when
all is said and done, one trusts only oneself.

Other people gave up the chance to lie around on the beach,
not out of personal choice but because many of the resorts and
sanitoriums, which are administered by the trade unions for
their members, rescheduled their time to make room for the
residents of the radiation zone and for Kievans, particularly the
children and mothers of young infants.

The simplest and most important way of protecting oneself
from the radiation—and this was true on a daily basis for

everybody who had been exposed to the accident at the plant and for residents of Kiev and its environs—was cleaning with water. Not only did everybody shower, but everything, including the streets, the trees, the stores, and the markets, were "showered" several times a day. A regimen of closed windows and of cleaning apartments with water was followed by everyone. The objective was not mere cleanliness but sterility. Special laundries and dry cleaners were opened so that clothing and bedding could be decontaminated. One Moscow laundry converted its operations to decontaminating the clothing and bedding for all city hospitals where rescue workers at the nuclear plant were being treated. The first loads of laundry to arrive at the cleaners had to be destroyed. The rest was washed. The amount of work was enormous. Bedding was changed in hospitals three times a day—not only sheets and pajamas, but blankets as well. A special laundry decontamination process was developed that lowered the radioactivity 120 times and greatly shortened the cleaning time. Special protective clothing and individual dosimeters were distributed to the laundresses doing the work.

The specialized dry-cleaning operation experienced its share of curious moments. After an announcement in the newspapers of the work going on, people started pouring in, carrying bundles of clothes; the rumor had spread that anyone who wanted to could bring his or her clothes there. Actually, the order was meant only for those who had come from the stricken areas and were directed by their doctors to have their clothes dry cleaned.

Subsequently, dosimetric testing was introduced in all laundries and dry-cleaning operations of Moscow, and not a single case of radioactive contamination was found in the clothing of any Muscovite.

Much discussion and idle rumor burned around what damage might be suffered by the Ukraine, historically one of the most agriculturally productive areas of the Soviet Union. Obviously the damage was great, and only time—a lot of time— would help to set right the agricultural harm wrought by the nuclear accident.

Today, the distribution of radioactive fallout in the soil around the Chernobyl plant is uneven, since weather has played a role in spreading fallout. There is an arbitrary thirty-kilometer radius around the plant, but there are contaminated areas beyond it, and relatively uncontaminated areas within it. In those places where the fallout in the soil is comparatively shallow—a few millimeters deep—the upper layer of soil is being removed and carted away for burial elsewhere so that the fields can be returned to working condition. By mid-June, in fact, several fields in the Chernobyl Administrative District had already been returned to active agriculture. In places where contamination of the soil reaches deeper, special crops are being planted that are capable of drawing up the radioactive isotopes and decontaminating the earth; later, they'll be harvested and buried elsewhere. But there are many unresolved problems and questions involved in such an operation. Preventive measures are being made known to the farmers and field hands within the thirty-kilometer zone and in certain places outside it. For example, outdoor workers are required to wear gloves and use respirators. Workers are advised not to be too casual about the dangers. The degree of contamination in particular localities is being pinpointed as precisely as humanly possible, since the topography of a radiation field is extremely uneven.

In all events, whether in terms of food, drinking water, or agricultural activities, there is really just one objective: to make all human activity as safe as possible, and not to allow any violation of the health standards that have been established.

5

THE EVACUATION:
How the People Abandoned Their Homes
and Where They Went

It's a sorry spectacle. The villages of the Chernobyl Administrative District are empty of people. The desolate city of Pripyat, along whose street a patrol car with extra radiation protection occasionally rolls, and the farms that once held livestock are now shut down.

Along the highway leading to Chernobyl, it's categorically forbidden to drive off the roads because of the danger lurking in the once ordinary but now radioactive dust in the eerily quiet woods and fields. Here on weekdays the woods used to be filled with people hunting mushrooms; on holidays they were downright crowded. As the residents say, "All Kiev used to come here on weekends."

All told, the accident forced the resettlement of almost 100,000 people. They were evacuated quickly and peacefully. In part this calm could be explained by the hope—almost the certainty—that they were abandoning their homes for only two or three days or maybe a week at most. Time has passed. It has now become clear from observed data that certain parts of the thirty-kilometer zone are still considered potentially dangerous, though the level of radiation hasn't risen, even on bad days. The possibility of returning is still far away.

Today the people of Chernobyl (for that's what I call everyone who was evacuated from anywhere inside the thirty-kilo-

meter zone) live mainly in four other districts of the Kiev
Administrative Region. Everyone has a roof over his or her
head, everyone has been given free financial assistance, and
everyone has been given a job. Because of the special circumstances, everyone is being paid at a level at least as high as his
or her previous average earnings.

How was all of this accomplished?

I remember the brilliant, sunny spring days at the beginning of May. Buses jammed with people were hurrying away
from Chernobyl. Farm trucks towed trailers with cows mooing
and sheep bleating. The exodus didn't engender a feeling of
chaos despite the fact that there were many problems surrounding the resettlement of such a large number of people.

It wasn't a matter of transporting people just anywhere; at
their destinations there had to be ready housing, medical care,
groceries, bathing facilities, baby food, etc. There were a hundred thousand little details to be taken care of.

Recalls G. Revenko, the head of the Kiev Regional Party
Organization: "At first we decided to evacuate a zone within a
radius of fifteen kilometers. But as the specialists examined the
situation and determined the radiation levels for all the villages, hamlets, fields, and forests more precisely, it was decided
to double the radius to thirty kilometers. We removed everyone
within that circle. It was expanded to provide an extra margin
of safety, because in the final analysis, the concern was for the
health of the people."

In the final analysis the Kiev Administrative Region encountered a misfortune that was without precedent. The complex nature of the circumstances was exacerbated by people
who weren't just taking suitcases with them: they were taking
cattle and poultry. And who would leave behind his dog to die?

In the end it wasn't just a matter of saving everything; it
was a matter of giving help to everyone. In most cases this
was done.

The Village of Razvazhev was one of twelve in the
Ivankovsk Administrative District that took in evacuees. It is
the seat of the Ukraine Collective Farm. It has a school, an arts
center, a library, and a hospital.

I talked with Aleksandra Davidova, a retired worker in the
day care center:

"When the buses began appearing with all these people, we recognized—especially the older folks did—that there had never been an evacuation quite like it before: the people just kept coming and coming. Well, everyone's got to live, don't they? So, we prepared to take in the new arrivals. I took in Mikhail Vozny and his family. It's not such a small family: there's his wife, Galina, and two kids, one in the fourth and one in the eighth grade. From the time they came I shared with them what I could. Soon groceries were trucked in and given to us free of charge. When the Vozny family entered my home I was asked, 'How long can we count on being here?' And I answered, 'As long as necessary.' "

Collective Farm chairman A. Radchenko told me, "That's pretty much the way all our people were. You can see for yourself."

I walked around the village, whose population in a matter of hours had risen sharply. Here are my notes after checking out just a single block.

Evdokiya Otroshenko, the laboratory director at the Collective Farm's animal husbandry operation, took into her home Valentinaw Bryukhanova, the wife of the nuclear plant's director. Bryukhanova immediately began working as a milkmaid.

Galina Kyksenok, a teacher at a local school, took in two families under her roof, five people in all, including the family of Valintina Popova. They all began preparing their meals and eating together.

The Ukraine Collective Farm gave out May Day presents to 200 little children who came to Razvazhev with their parents from Pripyat. By May 6 the village's new residents were receiving their first paychecks.

Forty-seven villages in the Polessk District of the Kiev Region took in evacuees, and there were twenty-three resettlement locations in the Borodyansk District. These figures reflect only the first few days of May.

Life doesn't return to normal immediately. On their first day in the Polessk District, 50 percent of the evacuated schoolchildren were at school. By the second day the figure was 90 percent. And all the children were in school by the third or fourth day.

I drove around to the places where the evacuees had gone.

On one trip I ran across an unexpected obstacle: a policeman waved his baton and ordered my car to slow down. I realized it was an unannounced checkpoint on the highway to Kiev. I was in a column alongside trucks, refrigerator-trailers, and Volga automobiles. I understood: a gigantic city sustains a heavy stream of traffic. Fresh produce, manufactured goods, and whatnot for hundreds of plants and factories are transported here. The effects of the Chernobyl accident could not be allowed to interfere with the normal rhythm of work in the capital of the Ukraine. It followed that every vehicle had to be examined for radioactive contaminants.

When my turn came, I slowly rolled up to the specialists with Geiger counters who were conducting the dosimetric monitoring. I got out of the car. The wheels and body of my Lada read within the acceptable range. The meters indicated the absence of radioactive contamination. However, they tested us as well, giving special attention to our shoes. And that was as it should have been: a reporter wanders all over hill and dale collecting material.

I asked the policeman about his work. He smiled.

"I'm afraid it'll disappoint you," he said. "I don't have any sensational stories to tell you. Practically every vehicle en route to Kiev has been clean. But that doesn't mean that we can go and drop the monitoring. The situation demands a high degree of vigilance."

While standing in the line of cars, I noticed another difficulty in the policeman's work. He was being tactful. There were too many opportunities to raise his voice or to start barking orders at people. A long line makes drivers nervous. Understanding the situation, the police and drivers were trying to keep their emotions under control. Eventually people got used to the checkpoints, and drivers stopped saying, "I haven't been anywhere near the nuclear power plant; why do you have to check me?"

One day I found myself in the Makarovs Administrative District, where life was stressed by a double burden. Evacuees had landed here, as elsewhere, but food production had to be increased.

I was told by Mr. Kozhukhovsky, chairman of the Makarovsk District Political Committee: "You can imagine the complexity of the situation just by recognizing that our bread-baking plant has doubled its normal output; we're now baking twenty-four tons of bread every day."

At the beginning of May the trade unions offered the evacuees financial assistance totaling 370,000 rubles,* 2,000 complete sets of clothes, 1,500 cloth articles, and 4,000 wool articles. This was just one of the shipments donated to the victims.

To capture a sense both of the situation and of how the various governmental ministries dealt with it, here are a few more statistics. The evacuees were given numerous items on credit without having to make a down payment. This included 16,400 sets of sheets and pillow cases. Furniture was provided where required: 3,800 beds and cots, 3,500 mattresses, 62,000 rubles' worth of dinnerware, and 300 portable gas stoves. Since the evacuees' condition demanded special attention, care had to be given to continued showers and cleanliness. The evacuees were given 8,500 tons of soap and detergents.

Mothers and children were given places in the Kiev Region's various health centers and rest homes, and placed in treatment and prevention sanatoriums. Later on, room was also made for them at the best resorts in the country, those in the Crimea and in the Caucasus Mountains.

I returned to the Makarovsk District. On the day I got there, a new group of people from the radiation zone was being processed, two evacuees to each household or farmstead.

I was surprised at the amount of paperwork. Forms had been printed especially for the occasion. On these sheets the new arrivals had to fill in their age, sex, place of residence, profession, and number of children. It soon became clear that that was exactly what had to be done during an emergency evacuation. Why? To minimize the difficulties of finding people the right jobs and to make certain there is enough food for their youngsters. This work would also assist the relatives to locate families who had been evacuated.

From time to time, unusual problems cropped up—unusual, that is, for a city dweller like me. Take the cattle, for instance. In all, 17,446 head of cows, sheep, and pigs were brought to the Makarovsk District and distributed among nine

*1 ruble = U.S. $1.20, official rate.

local collective farms. Suddenly, these farms were faced with the problem of milking the additional cows and, what's more, feeding all the animals. The local farmers only had provisions for their own animals. But the farmers didn't do the obvious and start slaughtering the animals for meat. They sorted things out by carting in additional feed from other locales, and they reoutfitted their farms or built new structures from scratch. Everyone understood that a farmer couldn't manage his farm without his animals.

Careful consideration was given to placing people in their new homes. For example, a carpenter would be matched with a carpenter, and a milkmaid with a milkmaid. The chairman of a collective farm would be billeted with another chairman, and a foreman with a foreman. Because of the time they spent together at home, they had the opportunity to come to mutually satisfying terms about how they could work together. The results were excellent. The evacuees had little time for rest: a multitude of problems had to be solved by them together with their hosts.

Now each household of the Makarovsk District became two households. There wasn't a minute to waste before the tractors went back into the fields; corn and grain had to be planted, because winter is a harsh judge. There were many more mouths to feed in the district.

One subject of discussion during the summer that astonished me was the serious debate over how the new settlers would feel come autumn, and apropros of that, over new housing construction and, in general, over enlarging the district's economic base.

At first glance, there seemed to be a million more urgent problems. For example, the evacuation of people from the thirty-kilometer zone was still going on. Not everyone was established and well fed. The new settlers, having left homes where they and their families had grown up, had no idea that someone was facing the questions of actually building them new homes and creating jobs.

Few of them realized how terribly complex and protracted a process it would be to travel a short distance from Chernobyl to Ivanovsk, Makarovks, Polessk, and Borodyansk.

They had left their troubles behind and hoped to return soon to a peaceful and uneventful life.

Meanwhile, in Kiev, tons of concrete, millions of bricks, and tracts of timber had already been assigned to the building of new settlements. Construction workers were recruited from the various regions of the Ukraine not directly affected by the accident. Many of these workers had actually volunteered for the jobs.

In short order nearly 50,000 construction workers started erecting dozens of new settlements. The deadline for completion of the construction was set for September 1: everything had to be ready by the first day of school.

The entire evacuation proceeded in an orderly manner without panic. That is not to say that it didn't affect people. The evacuees had to confront the fact that they might not return to the homes they had grown up in.

And during this whirlwind of resettlement people occasionally lost track of their kith and kin.

For many people the evacuation was a heavy, painful, stressful blow that in turn led to sleepless nights. But they rose to the challenge.

I give my thanks to the people who so kindly took in the evacuees and helped them cope with the hardships of setting down new roots.

■ ■ ■

I noticed that the farther I got from the site of the accident, the more heated the discussions over the real—and frequently the imagined—problems, complications, and dangers that the ill-fated Reactor No. 4 had thrust upon the people who lived around it.

I would like to discuss a few of them in the following chapter.

6

CHERNOBYL, THE MYSTICISM, 1986
CHERNOBYL, THE REALITY, 1986

> The third angel sounded, and there fell a great star from heaven, burning as it were a lamp, and it fell upon the third part of the rivers, and upon the fountains of waters;
> And the name of the star is called Wormwood: and the third part of the waters became wormwood; and many men died of the waters, because they were made bitter.
>
> Revelation 8:10–11

To the Russian ear, the word Chernobyl is rich in meanings and tones. *Chernyi* means black or dark; and *byl*, a story. The two roots and their component parts nudge the Russian ear into associations and consonances. So similar is the sound *byl* to the word *bol* (pain) that in newspaper headlines and ordinary conversations the name of the small Ukrainian town of Chernobyl seemed to take on a symbolic meaning.

It also became clear that in Chernobyl the word *byl*, though linked historically with the words for being or existence, had another association: a botanical one. *Bylka*, or *bylinka*, is a blade of grass. And the *chernaya bylka*, or *chernobyl*, is another name for wormwood.

The rules by which a rumor spreads are mysterious, but the process is swift. The lines from the Revelation of St. John the Divine in the Bible are known by practically everyone. The connection between Chernobyl and the Revelation was suggestive.

Centuries ago, hordes of people would prostrate themselves and spread their arms to the heavens when there was an eclipse of the sun, the eruption of a volcano, an earthquake, or a flood; all such events would induce horror because they "represented" divine punishment for the sins of humanity. Alas, humanity has become no less sinful during its long history. We have, however, remained superstitious. It is true that at an eclipse of the sun we no longer look for divine explanations; eclipses are predictable. But the various results of our exploitation of the atom has, in the ignorant, suddenly given rise to forgotten associations.

However, the bright light of knowledge glows proudly in the workings of the mind. Filaret, the Metropolitan of Kiev and Galicia,* spoke of superstitious gossip and speculation in the following manner:

"Man cannot know the dates outlined in the Book of Revelation. Jesus said, 'The hour and day of the Apocalypse is not known to the son of man, nor to the angels, but to the Father alone, that is the Lord.' The Book of Revelation can be applicable to different times, and in the course of two thousand years there have been a good number of situations that could have been said to match the revelations of St. John. At each of those times there have been people who have said, 'See, then, truly the time has come.'

"But here we are, the second millennium is already coming to a close, and the time has still not come. And if it should come, it will not be given to man to know.

"What is more, whether that time is drawing nearer or receding depends finally on man himself. Today we are witnesses to the fact that mankind has the capacity to annihilate itself. There are atomic weapons, and in a quantity sufficient to blow up the entire planet. But with good will we have the capacity actually to eliminate nuclear weapons? Everything depends on the moral stature of all mankind. If, in a moral sense, man can exist on the level that he is capable of, then he will not only not resort to the use of nuclear weapons but he will actually eliminate them. In this way, what is written in the Book of Revelation—'the time'—can be held off for a long time."

*In the Russian Orthodox Church, a Metropolitan is a bishop ranking just below the patriarch who serves as the head of an ecclesiastic province.

"People believe nothing so firmly as the things they know nothing about," as the wise Montaigne once said. The Metropolitan of Kiev proved again the fairness of this thought: ignorance does not become any less ignorant just because it hides behind a quotation from Holy Scripture.

Similarly, a misfortune is no less terrible if its explanation can't be found in the Bible. And it should be said that the Russian Church, by not seeking the easy way and preaching the end of the world, actually helps the country to cope with misfortune.

Added Metropolitan Filaret:

"As early as 1927, Father Sergius said that the Church must share with the people both joy and sadness. So it was during the Second World War, and so it was in times of peace—and so it is today when extreme misfortune befalls our country. The Church does not separate itself from the people, but rather believes that this, the people's sadness, is its sadness; this grief is its grief.

"Together with the people, we believe that we must not only endure this misfortune but elevate the spirit of the people. Because the spirit can triumph over many things. But the contrary is just as true, and depression or despair can be manifested in a person's health.

"One of the tenets of the Russian Orthodox Church is also that the clergy sacrifice monetarily to aid the victims of an accident.

"I have received many expressions of sympathy and brotherly love in letters and telegrams from abroad. But many of these letter writers seemed at the same time to have fallen under the influence of Western propaganda. We expressed our regret that they had succumbed to slander and lies directed at undermining trust in the Soviet Union. From a Christian point of view, it is morally despicable to build politics on human sorrow."

Over the summer Theodosius, the Archbishop of Washington, the head of the American Autocephalic Orthodox Church, and the Metropolitan of the United States and Canada, came to Kiev. "As Christians," he said, "we have compassion for people who were at Chernobyl. We pray for the health of those who survived and for those who have gone to their eternal rest. Your joys are our joys, your grief is our grief. We are filled with compassion, and not only we, but also the other Christian people of America, who understand your misfortune."

Both men, the Metropolitan of Kiev and the Archbishop of Washington, sympathizing with the people who found themselves in trouble, also touched on the necessity of accord between nations. Any normal person can't fail to agree with the holy fathers. The only conclusion we can draw from the Chernobyl experience is that a nuclear war would be a thousand times more terrible.

History offers the richest possible opportunities for linking causes and effects in mystical chains. But it's not only lovers of such historical-geographical exercises who'd like to find out more about Chernobyl.

The first mention of the village of Chernobyl dates from manuscripts of the twelfth century A.D. But settlements at the site are known to have existed considerably earlier: twenty-eight burial mounds have been found nearby containing iron weaponry. At the beginning of our own century a treasure of silver Roman coins from the time of Mark Antony was uncovered. At different times the land belonged, first, to Poland, then to the Ukraine. The residents of Chernobyl were boatmen, fishermen, and gardeners. Besides other vegetables, they exported mountains of onions. They sold timber, tar, tobacco, and fish. There were tanneries and brickmaking plants, two parochial school, and mills. Its population of 14,500 was bigger at the turn of the century than it is today.

The religious history of the village was also a rich one: there were two Orthodox churches, one Catholic church, and, until 1832, a Dominican monastery. The so-called Old Believers settled there during the second half of the eighteenth century, and later the sect began calling itself Chernobylite. The head of the sect, Illarion Petrov, bore the rather strange nickname "Cow's Legs" and was known for his extreme fanaticism. The sect preached the imminent arrival of the Antichrist and the end of the world. The authorities of the time had reason to interfere with the activities of Illarion's followers: the sect refused to pray for the tsar, did not acknowledge passports, forbade military service and oaths, and behaved in a contrary manner. Therefore, in all probability, it didn't take much convincing when, at the end of the eighteenth century, they decided to migrate to Austria. They had been invited by Emperor Josef II, who also freed the Old Believers from taxation for twenty years. The extremely kind offer by the Austrian emperor was connected with an unknown but apparently important service that the Chernobyl sect had rendered to a certain distinguished Austrian nobleman. Subsequently, the members of the Chernobyl sect mixed with other emigrants from Russia and Poland, and their history faded among the other events of the stormy nineteenth century.

If a person wants to look for a symbolic connection between the dark preachings of Illarion the Cow's Legs and twentieth-century atomic energy, that's his business. Chernobyl is just a tiny little spot on the stamping grounds of Europe.

The history of peoples and languages on this territory intertwined. And any patch of Europe, any rivulet or tiny village would give us ample material for associations and folklore. So then, there can be but one symbol here: in the history of Chernobyl is intertwined the lives of Ukrainians, Poles, Russians, and Austrians, royalty as well as peasants.

While the people of Chernobyl move out of their homes, perhaps forever, scientists and workers move in for the massive clean-up. The danger of radiation is ever present in the dust, in the shrubs and on the roads.

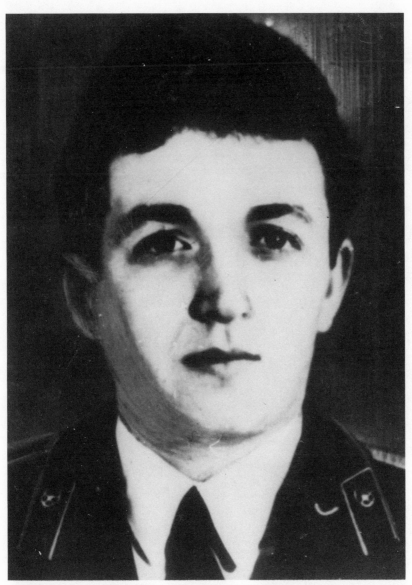

FIREMAN VICTOR KIBENOK, 22, WAS POSTHUMOUSLY
AWARDED HIS COUNTRY'S HIGHEST HONOR, THE ORDER OF
HERO OF THE SOVIET UNION.

FIREMAN VLADIMIR PRAVIK, 22, ONE OF THE FIRST TO BATTLE THE FLAMES, WAS ALSO AWARDED HIS COUNTRY'S HIGHEST HONOR POSTHUMOUSLY.

PRIPYAT, THE ONCE-BUSTLING CITY WAS HOME TO THE NUCLEAR ENERGY WORKERS—NOW IT IS DESERTED. NO ONE KNOWS WHEN ITS INHABITANTS WILL RETURN.

VLADIMIR OKHRIMOVICH, 88, STILL REMEMBERS WORLD WAR I. RELUCTANT TO LEAVE HIS VILLAGE, A RESCUE WORKER JOKES HIM OUT OF STAYING.

PREGNANT WOMEN AND VERY SMALL CHILDREN WERE
PLACED IN A HEALTH SANITARIUM.

AS POPULATION MOVES INTO OTHER AREAS, THIS
COOPERATIVE FARM DISCOVERED IT HAD TWO PRESIDENTS
AND TWO TRACTOR DRIVERS.

WEEKS AFTER HE DIRECTED THE EVACUATION EFFORTS IN
THE IVANOVSK REGION, VLADLEN BABIKOV WAS STILL HARD
AT WORK.

THIS BUILDING IS HEADQUARTERS FOR THE GOVERNMENT
COMMISSION. IT'S DIFFICULT TO DISTINGUISH THE DOCTOR
FROM A WORKER OR MINISTER.

SOVIET SOLDIERS WORKED ON THE CLEAN-UP FROM THE VERY FIRST DAYS. HERE IS A DETACHMENT NEAR THE STRICKEN PLANT.

RELAXING WITH A CIGARETTE, VALERI IGNETENKO WORKED INSIDE THE RADIATION ZONE. HE IS A MEMBER OF THE ARMY'S CHEMICAL DEFENSE CORPS.

THE MAIN METHOD OF TRANSPORTATION WITHIN RADIATION
ZONE IS THE ARMORED CARRIER.

AN URGENT CALL SENDS RESCUE WORKERS SCURRYING TO
THE ARMORED CARRIERS.

A TRACTOR THAT CAN WORK BY REMOTE CONTROL ARRIVING AT CHERNOBYL; ITS CABIN IS OUTFITTED WITH EFFECTIVE DEFENSES AGAINST RADIATION.

CONTROL POINT ON THE ROAD BETWEEN CHERNOBYL AND KIEV.

EACH SIDE OF THE ROAD, WHERE RADIOACTIVE DUST ACCUMULATES, IS BEING COVERED WITH A SPECIAL SEALANT FILM.

BULLDOZERS REMOVING TOP LAYER OF SOIL WHICH IS
CONTAMINATED WITH RADIATION; SOIL WILL BE SENT TO A
BURIAL SITE.

THE LAST CONTROL POINT BEFORE THE RESTRICTED ZONE.

DUST IS THE MAIN CARRIER OF RADIATION WITHIN THE REACTOR ZONE, WHICH IS WHY THE ROADS ARE CONSTANTLY SPRINKLED WITH WATER AND NOT ALLOWED TO DRY OUT.

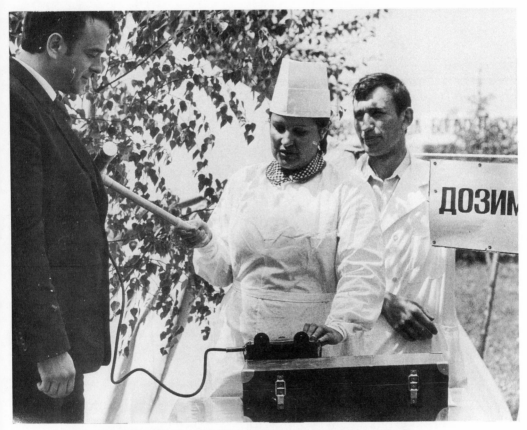

NO ONE IS PERMITTED TO LEAVE THE REACTOR ZONE
WITHOUT BEING CHECKED WITH A DOSIMETER (GEIGER
COUNTER).

EVERY VEHICLE LEAVING RESTRICTED ZONE IS TREATED
WITH SPECIAL DE-CONTAMINANT LIQUIDS. THIS PHOTO WAS
TAKEN THROUGH A CAR WINDOW.

HOT FOOD WAS SUPPLIED TO WORKERS 24 HOURS A DAY. HERE ARE SEVERAL COOKS AT A FIELD CAMP.

DR. ROBERT GALE OF CALIFORNIA, LEFT, WHO VOLUNTEERED
HIS MEDICAL SERVICES TO RUSSIA, IS SHOWN HERE BEING
INTERVIEWED BY IZVESTIA CORRESPONDENTS ANDREY
ILLESH, CENTER, (AUTHOR OF THIS BOOK), AND BORIS
IVANOV, RIGHT.

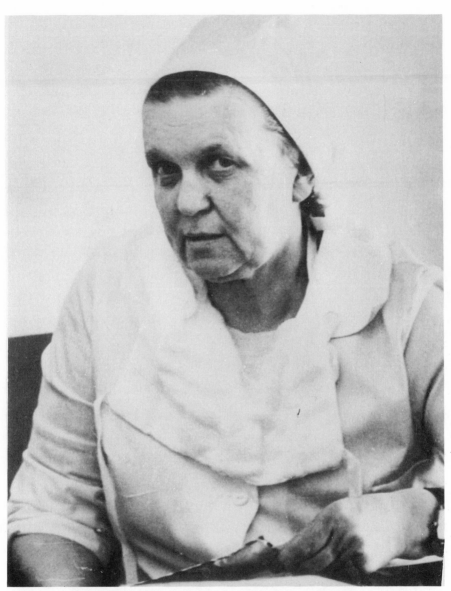

PROFESSOR ANGELINA GUSKOVA, ONE OF RUSSIA'S LEADING AUTHORITIES ON RADIATION, SUPERVISED MEDICAL TREATMENT OF PATIENTS WITH RADIATION SICKNESS.

FIRE MARSHALL TELYATNIKOV, WHO SUPERVISED THE
EXTINGUISHING OF THE FIRE AT THE CHERNOBYL NUCLEAR
POWER STATION ON THE TRAGIC NIGHT.

TRACTOR BEING WORKED BY REMOTE CONTROL AT THE
STRICKEN PLANT.

WORKERS IN PROTECTIVE GEAR, HEADING FOR WORK.

HELICOPTER, HOVERS OVER STRICKEN PLANT, DROPPING
SAND AND LEAD.

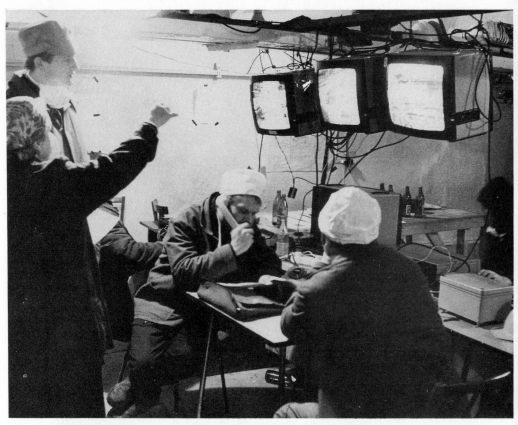

SUPERVISORS USE TELEVISION CAMERAS TO MONITOR
PROGRESS.

7

RADIATION AND THE BIOSPHERE:
Prognoses, Suppositions, and Actions

The Chernobyl accident presented ecologists, botanists, and zoologists with two extremely difficult problems: (a) to find out exactly what happened and (b) to figure out whether what happened could be surmounted. Research by the Ukrainian Botanical Garden showed that the radiation had been distributed unevenly. The particles stuck to the northern side of the trees facing the accident site. Plants with sticky or rough leaves, for example, velvet peach trees, absorbed large amounts of aerosols; yet for some unknown reason the peach trees were almost entirely free of contamination. Such are the paradoxes of nature. What's more, many of those paradoxes are being encountered for the very first time.

In the opinion of the director of the botanical garden, Academician Grodzinsky, it's going to be necessary to purify the planet of radioactive wastes to help the biosphere cope with the costs of technological progress.

The products that formed in the nuclear reactor began to melt down, boil, and be released into the air in the form of tiny particles—mere microns in size—containing radioactive atoms. As a result, radioactive ash was released into the atmosphere. The heavier particles settled nearer the site; the lighter ones were carried off by air currents. Aerosol mixed with dust stuck to leaves and grass and settled onto soil, asphalt, and water. The most unpleasant aspect of this situation is that ash was inhaled by people and animals.

In the first stage the physical properties of an aerosol are the most important factor; the actual chemistry of the constituent atoms doesn't yet play any role. The particles simply stick to one surface or another and, in decomposing, give off invisible alpha, beta, and gamma rays in every direction. However, the danger depends on the actual dose, its biological effects, and how long it lasts.

To a marvelous degree, the springtime woods came to our assistance: the young sticky leaves, needles, twigs, bark, bushes, and grass helped absorb the injurious aerosol that was driven by the winds. For that reason the background radiation in the forests was three and four times higher than in Kiev.

It would be nice to believe that the accident will have no really serious after-effects. For many living things, such radiation may even induce growth, and indeed in certain places many people have noticed an unusually beautiful flourishing and lush growth of many plants and grasses.

Moreover, in many places in nature the normal background radiation is quite high, yet there have been people living there since time immemorial. For example, many medicinal springs, among them a good number right in the Ukraine, possess a high degree of natural radioactivity. They include the radon waters of Belaya Tserkov and Mironovka and the famous springs of Mirrad-Mirgorod.

For trees and bushes in the forest the present level of radiation is not so great an evil when compared with those misfortunes that they are constantly suffering at our hands. Chemical contamination of forests is a far more serious matter.

In the second stage, the chemical properties of radionuclides start to make themselves evident and an enormous biogeochemical process begins. At first the particles simply adhere to any surface; further travel is a function of the chemical peculiarities of the given atom or molecule. Those that coincide chemically with the nutrient substances of plants penetrate the plant tissues and become incorporated in the foodstuffs that are important for our own diet. A large part runs off onto the ground, where it is absorbed by the forest litter. This is good, insofar as it retards the further migration of the particles into the ecosystem. Many radionuclides enter rainwater, and from there the ponds and lakes. Luckily nature has a means of defending itself: many radioactive elements drop in the water and join the bottom silt. The radioactive elements don't disappear altogether, but while they are in this "buried" state there is time for them to decay gradually.

But even here there's no avoiding certain problems. Some microorganisms, such as fungi and algae, and certain plants and animals possess an inexplicable passion for "devouring" particular substances. They go out of their way to devour their "favorite" atoms from the water and soil and accumulate high concentrations of them in their own tissues.

Different plants behave differently when subjected to radioactivity. They assimilate the isotopes of zirconium from contaminated layers of soil, and to a very small extent, they pick up and incorporate yttrium and certain other elements. Legumes, for example, are more voracious in this regard than cereals. Seeds are ten to twenty times less radioactive than stems. In potatoes, the tops become more radioactive than the tubers, although after the tops wither these substances begin to migrate to the tubers and roots. A great deal depends on the nature of the soil itself. For example, plants that grow best in clayey sand contain seventy times more strontium 90 than the ordinary sand, and plants that grow in loam contain as much as forty times and as little as fifteen times the amount.

But this strange property of plants can be used to purify contaminated areas and return them to agricultural use. For this purpose buckwheat, lupine, and other plants that possess similar selectivity toward the necessary radionuclides are sown. Then these plants are harvested and buried at depths of from two to three meters in places that are removed not only from the roots of other plants but from any ground waters. Though this method works, it is both time consuming and expensive. Another method is to sow crops that are unreceptive to the radioactive substances.

Nature can take care of a great deal on its own, but in this instance it can't manage without humanity's assistance.

The inhabitants of the stricken and bordering areas must observe the rules of hygiene and diet, and strict standards have been established for fruits and vegetables. The difficulty is that there is, on the one hand, carelessness and scorn for the existing danger and, on the other, the possibility of panic. Actually, in the summer of 1986 Kievans and others who live in the Kiev Administrative Region had to abstain from the forests' bounty, that is, from mushroom hunting and berry picking.

Among the radionuclides listed above one of the longest lasting and consequently one of the most dangerous to humans and other living things is cesium 137. Fortunately, this element doesn't migrate especially well through the ecosystem; it accumulates in bottom muds, in freshwater algae, and is absorbed by many plants and animals, but in small amounts. There is also a reliable way of diminishing its likelihood of contaminating plants. Chemically, cesium behaves like an alkaline metal and is analogous to phosphorus, which is so important to plant growth. Therefore, if plants can be fed corresponding amounts of phosphorus-containing fertilizers, their cesium content can be lowered practically to nil. As explained earlier, this is called element substitution.

Another dangerous element, strontium 90, tends to accumulate in bone; once it enters the body it's extremely difficult to eliminate. A diet that's high in calcium is usually recommended as a preventive measure. Zirconium 95, niobidum 95, rhodium, and rutenium are also dangerous isotopes; however, in humans and animals they can pass through the gastrointestinal tract without being retained by the body.

Another way of treating the soil is to fertilize it with lime, dolomite powder, and wastes from open-hearth furnaces. Then the deep layers of earth can be plowed under. Thus the topsoil is clean; the radionuclides bind to the lime and remain underneath. This method is especially good for Chernobyl, where the soils are of the podzolic sod, gray forest, and sandy types. They are low in organic content, and the radionuclides can quickly migrate.

In the opinion of the experts, the most efficient way to treat the zone immediately adjoining the nuclear plant was by dusting it from the air with calcium compounds. For one thing, this helped prevent migration of the aerosols. Other sectors not producing radionuclides could be sown with plants that help clean the soil.

In general, the most efficient way of dealing with the plots of land of least value is to let them remain fallow for a period of time before returning them to their natural vegetational distribution; the vegetational population in nature will build up the necessary organic compounds in the soil. The soil in these areas is the poorest in the Ukraine. The poor quality of soil was taken into account when choosing the site for the nuclear power plant.

In the elevated radiation zone, it is effective to change the kind of farm crops planted. It's necessary to use plants that won't pick up radionuclides. For example, rye absorbs significantly less strontium than does wheat. But especially good in this situation are commercial crops, which undergo processing. In the extraction of starch from potatoes, radionuclides are filtered out and the end product is perfectly harmless. Obviously, flax can be cultivated as well. The land around Chernobyl is also appropriate for perennial grasses, which show almost no effect from radionuclides.

Specialists have compiled detailed, four-color maps of agricultural lands. The area at the center of the thirty-kilometer zone where the radiation level rose to twenty milliroentgens in an hour is black; areas where the radiation is more than five milliroentgens but less than twenty are colored red; and the blue areas signify two to five. The rest of the land is rendered in green. There are other maps on which the exact distribution of strontium and cesium are marked in detail.

The maps are referred to whenever questions of agriculture have to be resolved. It's obvious from the maps that the contaminated areas are distributed spottily and unevenly. What is to be done with the black areas is crystal clear: the land must be removed from use, but for how long only time will tell. Observations of the land will be conducted constantly, along with the decontamination operations that were implemented immediately after the accident.

No crop whatever has been harvested from anywhere in the radioactive zone, even though there are relatively safe places within that area.

In the red zone, 24,000 hectares* of crops were left unhar-

---

*A hectare equals approximately 100 acres.

vested. Because the area was predominantly devoted to cattle and animal husbandry, these were feed crops.

Light blue and green zones border on the thirty-kilometer red zone. For them recommendations were formulated in which biological and climatological factors were taken into account. They also take into account allowances for the cattle feed and readying the soils for planting the following spring.

There are many problems to be resolved, so a multitude of experiments will be done to clarify the effectiveness of lowering the mobility of radionuclides, determining how harmful substances go from soil to vegetation, and how much are devoured by animals along the food chains. Science will be confronting a large number of these problems for the first time. As yet no one know why currants and gooseberries accumulate larger concentrations of radiation than other plants, while tomatoes, cucumbers, and radishes that were picked where the radiation was "hottest" turned out to be free of the slightest danger.

Chernobyl and its environs have a particularly large apple crop, so much so that many go unpicked. Since the emergency workers enjoyed eating these apples, one of the research physicists took it upon himself to conduct a painstaking study of the fruit. It became clear that as long as one removes the core one can eat three hundred kilograms of apples before one consumes even the minimum dangerous dose of radiation. Actually, no organized study of the Chernobyl apples has been made at this writing, but production in home garden plots in the surrounding villages has been the subject of special investigations. Detailed tables have been compiled, making it possible to calculate the degree of contamination of the fruits and vegetables from every sector, and the people have been given advice in gardening accordingly. Thus, in certain areas potatoes were absolutely fit for consumption, but digging them up had to be done with a degree of caution. That is, they had to be carried away immediately after they were dug up; they could not be left on the ground. The same procedure applied to apples and plums.

The crops of twenty-two villages were shown to present a real danger. However, through their local stores, the residents of those towns were fully supplied with vegetables trucked in from elsewhere. And if anyone from the other villages felt unsure about consuming their own products, they were advised to sell their crops as cattle feed.

It's impossible to answer all the questions about the future of agriculture in the red zone. Observations are expected to continue for some time.

8

THE LEVEL OF EFFORT,
CHERNOBYL AND PRIPYAT, MAY

I n the things that have been written about the Chernobyl nuclear accident, the phrase *radiation level* is repeated more often than any other. These frightening words tell the danger of working in the Chernobyl region. But there is another important level: the level of tension experienced by people who helped out during the aftermath. I'm convinced that this level includes the mobilization of all scientific and industrial forces directed at the stricken area.

I tried in vain to pry from the flight commander of the helicopter some information about any special feelings he might have experienced on the flight to the Chernobyl reactor while he was transporting the first members of the governmental commission there. The hearty young fellow tried to circumvent my question by offering clipped phrases: "It was fine. It was an ordinary picture. Fire? Didn't see any. Saw some smoke. Looked like what you see at any factory."

Neither he nor any of his colleagues gave the impression that they had done anything out of the ordinary. Maybe pilots have a right to call their work ordinary. But the job of the fliers, as prosaic as it may have looked, was urgently necessary from the very first day. They flew instruments that helped measure the radioactivity, and by the morning of April 26 they began working to plug up the radioactive volcano.

The aviators took a great risk. The work demanded extraordinary precision and mastery of flying. They had to measure the level of radiation over the reactor every day. On a forty-foot line affixed to the cabin of the helicopter hung an extremely accurate measuring device called a vacuum dosimeter. The pilots had to hover two hundred yards above the reactor, just enough time to activate the dosimeter. But they weren't allowed to touch it with their hands or to pull it into the cabin. Near the ground it was dropped onto a special platform. Then, hundreds of tons of lead shot, sand, and other materials were dumped from the helicopter into the gaping maw of Unit No. 4. Hundreds of flights had to be made to smother the reactor.

The road from Kiev to Chernobyl was changing before my eyes; from one day to the next it was becoming flatter. Potholes and cracks were filled with hot asphalt, making the road as good as new. Putting the road into ideal condition was a matter of safety. The radioactive dust and dirt dropping from the wheels of vehicles fell onto the roads. It was easier to wash it down if the highway was smooth and well-maintained. It had become clear from the beginning that the number of cars and trucks would be increasing. A decision was made not to drive every vehicle into the contaminated zone, but to unload them at the boundary checkpoints and consolidate the loads, lessening the number of vehicles to be decontaminated.

Decontamination: for most people this was their first encounter with the word. The scale and volume of this work was perhaps the greatest of all. First, it was necessary to solve the problem of fastest decontamination of localities. Otherwise it would have been impossible to work, as the risk would have been too great. Then it was the chemists' turn to develop a technology for spreading a compound film to cover contaminated surfaces. A fluid applied to surfaces hardened into a film that actually drew in the radioactive elements. After such treatment, the radioactive dust and particles could not enter the soil and water.

"The experimental activities of the scientists, and the discoveries they've already made here in the Chernobyl area, have been brilliant," said Mr. I. Silayev, the deputy chairman of the Council of Ministers of the USSR.

"Here's a typical illustration. One well-known international company, through intermediaries, offered their services for applying decontamination chemicals. For this they were asking $8,400 per kilogram. We very quickly started manufacturing an analogous fluid, in very large quantities, as much as 30 tons a day. It should be easy to figure the millions we saved. And the whole operation moved much faster. Imagine the effort a job like that demanded of everyone involved! Hundreds of thousands of square yards of the dangerous areas were covered daily. Aside from covering over the contaminated areas with polymerizing film, a method was also developed for pouring molten glass. It was particularly well suited for coating the roofs of buildings and other structures; there is no way water can wash it off."

These decontamination methods were used in the most dangerous places and are temporary, not permanent. In the future the film that absorbed the radioactive elements will have to be collected and buried. In several areas these operations have to be repeated two, three, or more times. This is a very labor-intensive method, and it's called "dry" decontamination.

Its virtue in comparison with other decontamination methods lies in the fact that it raises no secondary problems.

Problems do accompany the "wet" method of decontamination. It gives rise to a fluid runoff that can enter the groundwaters and river through the soil. The wet method is used for decontaminating roads, building, automobiles, and equipment; the contaminated water is then collected, purified, and deposited underground elsewhere.

That method was used in Bragin, an urban settlement in the Soviet Republic of Belorussia. The radiation level in this town of seven thousand wasn't high enough to evacuate the population, yet not low enough for people to continue living there safely. After lengthy consultations with doctors, scientists, and various specialists, it was decided that the town would not be evacuated, but everything had to be washed down: the houses, the barns, the garages, the warehouses, and even the trees.

A multitude of problems was encountered: where do you bury a two- to four- inch-thick layer of soil that has been removed along with its shrubbery? What do you do with the moss covering the slate roofs that didn't seem to be succumbing to the decontamination? How do you keep radioactive elements from entering the water?

All of the wells in the town were cleaned, then hermetically sealed. Every urban plot that could only be paved was covered with asphalt. All buildings that for one reason or another couldn't be washed were taken down. To make a long story short, there was a lot of work to be done.

In the Ukraine people who owned their own homes also took part in the decontamination efforts. When it was safe, heads of households who had been evacuated were taken back to their settlements. With the help of special brigades, they washed down their own homes and yards.

In other places, where the citizens couldn't help, certain homes required new roofs and/or walls. In Pripyat the decontamination of the city streets is being conducted by divisions of chemical defense forces. Soldiers dressed in special protective uniforms are doing the job with water and brushes, scrapers, and sometimes knives.

Heavily contaminated ground is simply removed. The upper soil layer is removed with bulldozers, loaded into special containers, and carted off to burial sites for radioactive wastes.

Decontamination work of a "deactivation" type is done around the power plant, and within the eighteen-mile zone. Obviously the work with the greatest danger is at the plant itself, at Unit No. 4.

As soon as it was possible to enter the plant, I did so and became the first journalist to watch where the emergency work was going on. And like the specialists entering for the next shift I experienced all of the safety measures: special clothing and footwear, a special transport vehicle, a "pencil" in the pocket of my jacket with which the radiation dosage could be determined, and finally, a personal examination. In preparation, I called V. Brezhnev, minister of transport construction of the USSR. It was his specialists, among others, who came to Pripyat immediately after the accident. They came from all corners of the country: subway builders, tunnelers, horizontal drillers from Kiev and Moscow; topographers from Kharkov, Gorky, Kuibyshev, and Dnepropetrovsk, and builders from the Baikal-Amur Railroad.

I came down from the headquarters of the governmental commission in a coffee-colored Volga, clean and sparkling, and not the sort normally used for dangerous work. But it had on its windshield a special pass, and next to this a red circle signifying the right to travel anywhere within the zone. We traveled the road from Chernobyl to the nuclear power plant. Alongside the road were fire trucks, huge bulldozers, busy people in special clothing; soldiers working or resting by tents set up like a checkerboard. Beyond the car's windows spring was in full bloom. Lilacs tumbled out from behind garden fences, seeking the sun. Gardens were covered in the white and pink of apple and cherry blossoms. The presence of an invisible danger was evident, as if underlined by the empty houses, the closed cattle sheds, the desolate streets and fields.

Pripyat was abandoned. A city in which homes and shops and streetlamps had become unnecessary . . . while men are on point-duty. It is quiet and ghostly.

A turn to the right led onto a road laid down miraculously in a four-day period. To go farther in the Volga would not have been possible. The car stopped at the administrative building of the nuclear power plant. At the entrance to the building our papers were checked. Then we went downstairs into the basement, where the operations headquarters had been.

People rushing to their shifts were all clothed in protective gear. I saw some resting on mattresses or sitting at a table and I heard the dominoes. A tall man dressed in special clothes stood up from behind one of the desks to greet me: "I understand you're from *Izsvestiya*."

My puzzlement was short-lived when I realized I looked like a white bird, with a Leica camera around my neck and a leather jacket, marking me immediately as an outsider.

"You'd better change your clothes," the minister said. I put on the necessary protective uniform, which included high-top shoes with curved rubber soles and straps at the ankles. The clothes would not only protect me from invisible trouble, they made me look like one of *them*, if only for a moment. It hid the fact that someone in the special zone wasn't immediately engaged in the actual emergency work. I felt like an intruder, although I knew I was the eyes and ears of the world.

The people around me, again riveted their attention to

their tasks, [aside from the medical personnel whose scrutiny of the needles on the "pencil"-type geiger counters, monitored all the workers].

But on that fateful day what exactly were the people doing who were working directly alongside the stricken reactor?

"From the back of Unit No. 3 of the nuclear power plant we dug a foundation area," explained the minister. "The crumbling earth we fortified with piles. One hundred fifty tunnelers came from Moscow accompanied by three drilling rigs. That was the most complicated operation—the horizontal drilling. The difficulty lay in the fact that we had to tunnel horizontally for a long distance. When everything was ready, we would be pouring nitrogen through these apertures; twenty-five tons a day were pumped through those pipes! At the other end of the pipes, the escaping nitrogen was developing a temperature of minus 120 to 130 degrees. The frozen soil would form a reliable barrier against radiation."

The entire trip to the base of the pit took about ten minutes. Yet we were just meters from the power plant, a few meters from the crippled reactor. This short road concealed visible dangers, but our driver was already an old hand at it; it was not his first trip, and in the most dangerous places he stepped on the gas. When we arrived, we climbed through the hatch of the personnel carrier, and jumped onto the ground. Behind us, like shelter, stood the wall of Reactor No. 3. Here in the pit around me people were working.

"This is the place for a camera!" I thought. No one had ever taken pictures of such a thing. But back in the basement of the administrative building the specialists, catching sight of my Leica, said, "Listen, friend, you shouldn't have brought it. They even took my watch: the radiation check later on will be tough enough." Maybe I shouldn't have been so protective with my editorial department's property? But it was too late for regrets. Now the notes scrawled in the notebook resting on my knees would be the only picture I'd get from the center of the special zone. (Even if I had taken the camera, the pictures probably wouldn't have turned out, since film spoils when exposed to radiation.)

We descended the sandy ground to where the drillers were.

At the rig the people turned around and shut off their equipment. Silence hung over the foundation pit. From the aperture of the newly opened passage a stream of liquid flowed, keeping the drill cool. The minister had a "special" talk with the driller. I had to overcome the awkwardness I felt as an intruder. Then I began talking with the people around me.

Now the workers were forced to lose time talking with me, when every minute counted. Their work was being regulated entirely according to the indications of the doctors' meters.

The tempo of the work, the speed of the drill that was penetrating into the depths of the foundation area underneath the reactor, determined the amounts of time allotted to the most important business. I'd been told in Chernobyl by Minister Silayev what this business was: "Building a 'cushion' under the entire area of the stricken unit creates a safeguard for us. This guarantee was brought about through the intensive efforts of metal workers, and foremen, and welders, and electricians."

But here the drilling rig started up again, filling the foundation pit with the noise typical of a construction site. I saw how the minister turned and raised his hand, thumb up. Then he explained that the shift had already dug thirty-three feet, which was outstanding. In its underground path the drill hadn't encountered any concrete barriers and was moving inexorably toward its goal.

A concentration of forces (and what forces!), made up of scholars, generals, lions of industry, and specialists at the top of their particular fields—these were "Chernobyl central." Staff decisions were being made right here. Many complex jobs were being put into operation, often for the first time anywhere. The top people, all masters of their trades, had responded to their nation's call and were here. The nationwide search for talent had not been in vain.

One thing I found strange: after I spent considerable time within one hundred yards or so of the crippled reactor, the sight of the meters registering high radiation didn't engender panic in me. And it was not because one adapts to any situation; it wasn't that at all. It was that *this* situation was such an extraordinary one: the circumstances that reigned in the foundation ditch gave rise to a kind of tranquility. Confidence was what came across—from Sergei, the driver from Chernigov bending over his steering wheel, someone who already knew every inch of the way to the reactor, and from the dozens who hurried past me through the glass doors of the administration building to their work. The matter-of-fact way all of these people went about their dangerous work was reassuring. It was being done with full awareness; they cognizant of every danger. Everyone understood too well what, in the final analysis, depended on their work, every hour of every day.

We meticulously wiped our feet with a rag that was lying in a zinc-plated box by the entrance to the administration building. There, in the corner, we pulled off the special plastic stockings we had had covering our shoes and pants. With the return of the shift the clothes mound was quickly growing. It would then disappear; all clothes contaminated with radioactive dust were removed immediately. Along with young men who were laughing over some local joke, I walked into the vast shower rooms. All clothing had been left below; you couldn't even keep a respirator or a white doctor's cap for a souvenir; the people with the dosimeters checking you out at the entrance and exit wouldn't allow it.

Standing under the shower, I caught myself examining the water. Sure, it was stupid; obviously you're not going to see any kind of radioactivity with the naked eye. But you still can't help trying to find something unusual. The medical check, however, showed nothing unusual; the reading on the dosimeters was normal—normal, it's true, for the special zone. But still people—many people—were living and working under these very circumstances.

Going downstairs, I saw more domino players. A man with a crewcut was enjoying some borscht straight out of a can and having what was by now an almost professional conversation with a topographer. The latter, trying to hide his professional pride behind irony, commented about the unfortunate nature of his job: "They're the first ones to arrive and do all the measuring. And then we sit it out until the work's all done. That's what I do: I sit and wait."

Of course he was just being humorous. He didn't wait around. Everyone was occupied with tasks that were important and urgent. For days on end skill, technical boldness, and vital decisions were demanded from a large number of people. The words *triumph, feat,* and *heroism* are synonyms for the same thing; in the special zone I never heard these words spoken, and yet what was being done there couldn't be described with any words but those.

It's enough to remember those days, that critical moment when the danger of a new explosion appeared. In the course of the first weeks after the accident, the possibility existed, because after the accident, even after the fire had been extinguished, the heart of the reactor, the active zone, continued to remain white-hot. Underneath the reactor was the reservoir. As a result of damage to the tubing of the cooling system, that reservoir had filled up with water. And it was impossible to exaggerate the danger if the nuclear fuel came into contact with the water. On top the reactor was covered with a heavy layer of sand, boron, and lead. And this created an additional weight on the unit's structure. Would it withstand the weight of this additional load?

The most pressing matter at that critical moment was determining how much water was in the basin, and how it could be siphoned off. Hundreds of fire trucks were pumping out the water. But to remove it from the basin completely in that manner was simply not possible. There was only one way to accomplish it: to open two valves in the pool itself. And they were located under the water. It should not be necessary to point out what kind of water this was.

This operation, which in any other situation would not have been terribly complicated, could be done only by human hands, under the very belly of the reactor, in the most dangerous part of the radioactive zone, in pitch-black darkness. And there were volunteers among the plant's personnel who did just that.

Only after it was completed could the governmental commission give the decisive conclusion: "The situation is under control." The possibility of experiencing another crisis had been eliminated.

C H A P T E R
9

SEVERE RADIATION INJURIES:
Who Treated Them, and How?

For some reason, certain medical specialties have come to occupy center stage. We all honor surgeons, cardiologists, pediatricians, etc., by their specialties, and undoubtedly they deserve it. But it also happens that their recognition comes from the patients who are saved. For example, because of orthopedic operations that returned certain stars to big-time sports, certain specialists became known to the public as great surgeons. However, these surgeons had been operating on injured people before they had ever appeared in newspaper articles—and had received thanks, but no sensational acclaim.

So it was that Angelina Konstantinovna Guskova had been doing what she did, and brilliantly so, long before the whole world had heard of her. But who adulates the radiologist? No one, until something occurs that is out of the ordinary.

The name of Professor Guskova was rather well-known in medical circles in the Soviet Union and abroad in connection with words seldom heard by most people: radiation injury, radiation sickness, and hematology. In May many people started hearing and saying those words.

The first time I ever saw Dr. Guskova she was surrounded by some of my fellow journalists. A unique press conference was going on in a specialized clinical hospital in Moscow where the most seriously ill of the victims of the Chernobyl accident were being treated. That was in May, when the doctors were under great strain because the majority of their patients were critical.

One could only guess at what it was like to be responsible for and care about every patient, to be exhausted beyond what you thought was humanly possible, with a fatigue built up during a month of sleepless nights. This modest woman didn't touch on the exceptional nature of what she and her colleagues had done. In fact, this extremely trying time had begun for them on April 26.

"Our clinic," said Guskova, "was instantly taken into the consultations. On April 26, at 4:30 in the afternoon, I was already on the telephone with the doctors in Pripyat. At 6 P.M. emergency planes were preparing to fly out. A couple of my colleagues were among the first people to spend time in Chernobyl.

"There's still no overestimating the importance of this first stage of the work, because with radiation sickness you can't delay. If you don't do the necessary operations within the first two weeks, they become unnecessary and we can't be of any more help. And after all, these aren't just operations; to transplant bone marrow, for example, you need a lot of time to prepare, to look for possible donors. The next day three planeloads of patients arrived here."

From that day forward the work of a small group of doctors began, doctors who had never before had such a large number of patients. Ten young doctors who just the day before had been junior staffers became the heads of ten departments. However, the most experienced physicians received the first, most seriously ill patients: the firemen.

During the war, the doctors on the front used to say that the bigger anything gets, the more complicated it becomes. When there are many wounded, there are never enough hands, never enough bodies, never enough minds to deal with them. Of course, there's no war now. And everything Guskova's clinic required for treating the victims, it received without delay: doctors, drugs, the most highly intricate equipment. And still it was the responsibility of the directors of the clinic, on Guskova's colleagues, to care for each person with every possible resource—as if that person were the only patient in the entire hospital. That was their slogan; that was the level of work they tried to maintain.

The doctors, the laboratory technicians, the nurses—everyone knew perfectly well that everything depended on their speed, their self-assurance, and their readiness to work grueling hours, despite their own fatigue. In the first days, until other hospitals could be found, a great stream of people arrived there for consultations and advice. No one was turned away, although the main concern was for those who lay in the wards. Nevertheless, three to four hundred analyses were done each day.

Every patient who was critically ill was watched around the clock by his own doctor and attended by a full-time nurse; the doctors worked in three shifts, the nurses in four. In addition, the hospital on-duty officer had a whole army on hand. All the petty grievances and misunderstandings were put aside. The only matter of any importance was the patient's interests. Guskova continued:

"The doctors at our clinic are warm, tender people. They offer contact that the patients find reassuring. The patients and the doctors got to know each other quite well—and by the way, I think that's an important element in their care.

"I should also point out that the patients were very active and very social, always interested in what the doctors were doing. That seemed to be true with even the very sickest of the patients, the ones who were in pressure chambers—though many realized they'd never return to their professional lives, and we found it very important that they occupy themselves with planning for the future. They were upset that we wouldn't let them work. But we still didn't know whether they would survive.

"We allowed those who were critical to see their loved ones. Some of the relatives became donors. The patients who were the very sickest worried about that: 'My mother's such an old woman, already, how can she do it? I can't take her bone marrow.'

"We understood the pain and anxiety of their relatives and friends; these were all young people, young families, wives, some who were expecting, and of these some of them for the first time. And all the same, we tried to keep visitors from the majority of the sick. After all, when a person has radiation sickness, even the visits of the doctors have to meet the most stringent possible sterile regulations. It's vital not to let even the slightest shadow of an infection into the wards."

But what *is* radiation sickness? Even in an uncomplicated form it's not easy to treat. It simultaneously attacks a whole spectrum of organs and systems. Depending on the dose of radiation received, various organs begin to break down first. Guskova's patients experienced the kind of exposures that hit more than just the hematopoietic—or blood-producing—system. It's the hematopoietic system that medical personnel know best. But in Chernobyl the magnitude of dose to some victims was such that it attacked the intestines and presented serious changes in other organs. And this was combined with extensive radiation burns to the skin. Even from the number of affected organs it became clear that a wide circle of medical specialists of different disciplines would have to be brought in to treat these patients. The leading doctors among them are hematologists, the specialists in blood diseases. But the specialists experienced in transplanting hematopoietic tissues, such as bone marrow, which manufactures blood cells, and the transplantation of fetal liver tissue—they are Americans. These doctors came to help and began working in Moscow in early May. Among those Americans was Professor Robert Gale.

Transplants of foreign hematopoietic tissue were done in a small group of the most critically ill. These operations, like any other transplants, are fraught with the danger of serious complications. The problem is that serious immune conflicts can occur if the patient retains any of his or her own hematopoietic tissue. The so-called host will reject the transplanted tissue, and in turn the transplanted tissue will start to fight the host. Therefore, the operation is contraindicated if the slightest hope exists that the patient's own capacity to manufacture new blood can be restored.

Guskova recalled:

"And nevertheless, moved by human feeling, and understanding that sometimes we can be too late in performing the transplant, we relaxed the guidelines for performing the operation. We did transplants even where the hope of living was uncertain from the very start. In these cases the chances of success were somewhat limited.

"More broadly, taking the radiation dose less into account, we used transplant of fetal liver tissue, having in mind that it's a less traumatic measure. We did that with the patients who were practically hopeless. But we considered that this operation wouldn't do any harm, wouldn't evoke immune conflict. When our American colleagues got here—the fourth and fifth of May—we had already completed six transplants on our own. With our American colleagues we continued this work.

"Of course, the presence of these very erudite specialists who had had worldwide experience was extremely useful."

In the first days the clinic admitted two hundred patients. Seventy were released fairly quickly. Of the remainder, according to Guskova, about eighty consumed the hearts and minds of the doctors. The decision of bone-marrow transplants was made for thirty-five of the most critically ill. Their medical histories were discussed jointly with the American physicians. These consultations proved very useful. All over the world mistakes in deciding the necessity of such transplants were frequently made. The method of introducing bone marrow in cases of uniform whole-body irradiation by a dose when a victim's own hematopoietic system could not be restored was developed for the first time by Soviet specialists in 1967. Therefore, the American doctors found the contact with their Soviet counterparts extremely useful. In the opinion of the American doctors, combining the efforts of Professor A. Baranov, a hematologist, and Professor Guskova, a radiologist, was a model synthesis of two disciplines that they hadn't achieved to date. They said that in the United States hematology and radiology exist quite apart from one another. For example, Gale had never been called to treat accident victims involving radiation. However, all the doctors were highly qualified specialists.

The transplants were done jointly. First the marrow donors were anaesthetized. In order to keep the time under anaesthesia to a minimum, the doctors withdrew the marrow from several different parts of the body. During the operation the doctors joked about a Soviet-American competition: which side was better at the procedure, and which was faster and kept the donor "under" the shorter amount of time?

Professor Guskova took special note of the tactful and

courteous manner of Dr. Gale and his associates. Whenever there were differences of opinion in the diagnosis or the prognosis, Gale would always cut the discussion short and say, "Stop. Let's end the debate and do as our hosts prefer."

Dr. Guskova was continually repeating the words *restraint* and *wisdom*, predominantly in situations where information about the patients or the course of treatment was inadequate:

"There are patients here whose lives we're concerned about. And any incautious word, especially when something might be said that mentions their names, where they might recognize their cases, can have a highly negative effect. Whether or not the world wants to see in our silence some sort of ill intention or unwillingness to share information is not the case. Although we studied the experience of the accidents that occurred in Yugoslavia and the United States, the arrival of such information is always tardy, despite differences in ethical standards.

"As far as summarizing our work and experience, which can be useful to any other country, we make it available to the scientific and medical communities. We should mention, too, that there's an agreement with Dr. Gale for some joint publications. But that will come only when we're no longer occupied every hour of the day with our patients."

These words—*restraint* and *wisdom*—dictated to Soviet physicians the necessity of limiting the participation by specialists from other countries in the treatment of patients with radiation sickness. Actually many rather insistently tried to come to join in the work and a very large number of companies sent their drugs. But still it would have been intolerable to have three doctors, whether Soviet or foreign, behind the attending physician, each one with questions. Interference, in some measure, would have begun to distract attending doctors from treating the patients. According to the decision of Guskova's colleagues, the sick were given only effective medications that had been previously tested and on which there was reliable scientific literature. These victims were not guinea pigs, and there was no need to experiment with them.

When I listened to Dr. Guskova, both at her first press conference and later on, I was struck by the calm assurance in her tone of voice, the deliberate choice of words and the care

with which she made decisions. It generated feelings of reliability and safety. I think that she inspired the same feelings in her
patients as well. And after all there were, there had to be,
moments of doubt, despair, and ultimately fatigue.

Angelina Guskova is the fourth member of her family to
work in medicine. Her great-grandfather, her grandfather, and
her father before her were all doctors. And her father was one of
the first physicians ever awarded the Order of Lenin, the highest honor in the USSR. Guskova herself entered the Sverdlovsk
Medical Institute in 1941, after World War II had already
begun. Her future profession was never in question when she
was growing up; what she would become was clear from
childhood. But World War II was also a war for physicians.
When he was called up to the front, before he left, her father
stopped to ask her, "Have you ever really stopped to think
about what you're getting into?"

Her will and character had been honed at home, and hard
years of wartime study strengthened them. The best qualities of
a doctor and of a human being—gentleness of spirit, wisdom,
toughness, and tranquility—became fully manifest in the way
that Guskova was able to go about her highly difficult specialty.

Although it wasn't a field she went into immediately, in the
early 1950s, in the Ural Mountains and later in Moscow,
Guskova began studying radiology, which was still a new field
at the time; she has spent the last fourteen years in a group in
this specialized clinic. In 1985 she wrote *The Organization of
Observations of Workers in the Nuclear Industry*. A chapter of the
book, "Accidents at Reactors and the Organization of Aid to
Their Victims," became the doctors' blueprint following the
Chernobyl catastrophe.

Guskova had also written a booklet together with some of
her colleagues. Not many copies were printed, and it was
written strictly for the Second World Congress of the Physicians
Against Nuclear War, in which Dr. Guskova is an active member. In her words, the booklet produced an impression like an
exploding bomb. Russians, perfectly independently, absolutely
objectively, meticulously, and in their own style interpreted the
possible consequences of a nuclear war.

But what distinguished this study from so many others? It
had no scenarios for war between two countries the way they

do abroad. The authors tried to emphasize that Europe is our common home; indeed, that our common home is the world; the danger is identical for everyone in it.

Another feature of the book was its system of computation. In it things were examined that many people found unexpected, such as the demographic aspect of the aftermath of the atomic explosions in Japan. After a conventional war, one usually observes a boom in the birth rate, and the demographic situation quickly balances out. In Japanese cities, by contrast, for the past twenty or thirty years, children have not only been dying young, but people to this day are afraid to have them. These conclusions were made for the first time, and the Japanese members of the Congress had the chance to evaluate them.

That Professor Guskova is the author of two such apparently different books has its own inexorable logic. To whom, if not to her, are the merciless, monstrous consequences of a worldwide nuclear catastrophe more obvious?

It's possible that during the joint operations, Guskova and her team also had a few minor differences with Dr. Gale, but on one fundamental question they were in full accord. The success with which all the therapeutic measures were performed and the relatively small number of fatalities were associated with the fact that there were twenty medical workers for every patient; that everything was done for every patient that could be done within the limits of modern medicine, whether in the areas of equipment, drugs, or the very timing of the hospitalization and surgery; and that the whole world was watching and sympathizing and helping. Fully fifteen countries made it known that they were ready to receive the victims of the accident, if the need arose. War, on the other hand, eliminates all the possibilities at the disposal of medical science in the world today.

There was yet another area in which the American and Soviet doctors came together: their joint work that summer allowed them to peek into the future and to get a sense of what it might be like if we collaborated with each other, in a time when the whole world, in amity, was concerned with the health of those who are ill.

"I am certain," said Dr. Gale, "that if this accident had

happened in some other country, Soviet doctors would have rushed to offer their help." Today, alas, it has become clear that not one country in the world is insured against such a tragedy, and that any government might find itself in need of the help of others in dealing with it.

So, who is this Dr. Gale, who by his own behavior gave the world an example of participation and cooperation? Dr. Robert Gale comes from California. Such a brief piece of information says little for those who, before April 1986, were never concerned with scientists. The name of the American bone-marrow transplant specialist, one of the major authorities in this most complicated field of medicine, is now rather widely known.

The terrible night when the accident occurred at Chernobyl called forth much newspaper scandalmongering. It also called forth the loftiest human and professional sentiments. Among the first people to volunteer their help to the victims of radiation in Chernobyl was Dr. Gale, and he was invited to come.

Our meeting took place in a room of the Sovietskaya Hotel that had become familiar to Dr. Gale. He had stayed there three times over a relatively short period.

Gale specializes in three areas simultaneously: oncology (the study of cancerous processes); hematology (diseases of the blood); and immunology (transplanting bone marrow). The last is only a small, albeit extraordinarily important, part of his work. He works with serious diseases that seem more common to the second half of the twentieth century, because they seem to be occurring with greater frequency. Oncology, hematology, and immunology are inseparably associated with bone-marrow transplantation. Similar operations are done in treating certain kinds of cancer and leukemia. The problems associated with treating cancer still await solutions. It is a field in which totally new ideas and methods are starting to appear. The treatment of leukemia, a part of which is bone-marrow transplantation, has always been in the front ranks of the ongoing war on cancer.

This dream, by the way—another of the things that Gale and Guskova find they have in common—this dream of conquering cancer, the most evil of our nemeses—is also what led the American professor to these problems at the frontiers of medicine. Dr. Gale recalled the beginnings of his work in this area:

"I did my first bone-marrow transplant in 1973. My first patient was . . . But why should I say 'was'? He's still alive! He was eight at the time—yes, only eight. His bone marrow had stopped functioning—a condition that's almost identical, really, to what happens with radiation poisoning. That is to say, radiation poisoning brings about a similar condition.

"In this boy's case, though, unfortunately, we didn't know what had brought the condition on. He had a five-year-old sister, who, we determined, had the very same bone-marrow tissue type. This fact became decisive. We did the transplant. That was thirteen years ago. Today the young man feels fine and goes to college. And his sister's eighteen and is a really pretty girl.

"All in all, I've done more than five hundred of these operations, the overwhelming majority of them at my clinic in the States. But I've also done surgery in Japan, Israel, and Latin America."

Shortish, wiry, and athletic, Gale looks younger than his forty years. He hears a question out and then answers it quietly, in a sure, even voice. You get the sense he has a lot of experience in "giving interviews." But despite this the scientist doesn't become dry or any less charming. The reason, apparently, is in his smile—sudden and generous.

There was a piano in the room and on it a violin in a case. Naturally, I asked him if he played and whether he's a music lover.

"Yes. I do love music. But it's my daughters who are the players in the family. And in Kiev, where I stayed with my whole family for a while, my daughters even gave a little concert in the hospital. Of course it was professional interest that drew me to the place, since they were treating children there who had been evacuated from Chernobyl. And in exchange for my daughters' music, they sang us some wonderful Ukrainian songs."

By the very fact that he had brought his whole family with him, Gale hoped to respond to what he felt to be the greatly overblown talk abroad of how dangerous life was in Kiev after the accident. He was sure that for many people this one act would be more comprehensible, and more convincing, than dozens of verbal assurances. Very likely he was right.

"In August I was in Kiev with my whole family, my wife and three children. As a doctor I can say that any level of radiation is not great. The Kievans were subjected to insignificant doses of radiation when the radioactive plume passed over the city. The risk at this point is really minimal. Really, I wouldn't have gone there myself, and I surely wouldn't have brought my family along, if I hadn't been so sure I was right." And he has a two-and-a-half-year-old son. "There can be no two opinions about it. I believe that now this city is absolutely safe and that people can live here completely without fear, and that includes children. Aside from that, the background radiation is getting lower and lower with every passing day."

Not only that, on his previous trip to the Ukraine, Gale had taken a helicopter right up alongside the Chernobyl plant. He wanted to see with his own eyes how the work was going on inside and around it: what kind of progress was being made in neutralizing the effects of the accident and how and under what conditions the workers and specialists were laboring to decontaminate the area. Seeing all of this first-hand meant being able to speak later on with that much more assurance. In Gale's opinion, it was essential for the scientists to know the actual situation; he saw no point in hiding anything.

The American professor thinks seriously about the prospect of working someday with his Soviet colleagues, about international cooperation in treating radiation sickness:

"Soviet medical people are just superb. In certain fields there's something to be learned from them. We also have our experience and our achievements. I'm convinced that by putting it all together we can make great strides. Concretely, here's just one of the many possibilities I see: the people that we and the Soviet doctors have treated jointly, and everyone who was put into the Soviet Transplant Center's national register, are now going to be entered into an international register. Just think how great it would be if we could combine all the bone-transplant registers in the world into one. The donor bank would be far more effective, and in turn we could help so many more people.

"The Chernobyl accident was not just a local event. National boundaries are no barriers to radiation. And in order to fight such tragedies and others like it successfully we're going to have to rely on international experience and international aid. The joint work of the specialists will help better than anything ever tried before to establish trust among professional physicians—and also, more generally, between nations.

"As a physician, I'm concerned with one thing more than any other: I believe that when God created the world, he couldn't have wanted little children to die of leukemia. And yet they do. They die. And I find that monstrous. I find it incredible. I am convinced that the time will come, that the day will arrive, when no one will die anymore from that horrible disease. We're trying to find the necessary ways and means to fight it. And to date we've accomplished some pieces of that. Today we're saving more than half the children with leukemia, whereas in 1945 practically every one of them would have died. But if the scientists of many countries would cooperate we could eradicate the disease altogether. Remember, people used to think tuberculosis was incurable, and polio was incurable, too. And look at them today. So, I'm optimistic about the future, and I think that some kind of antidote to cancer is surely going to be found. That's my dream."

Since acute radiation sickness runs a strictly limited course of two to two and a half months, the Soviet and American doctors have already analyzed the patterns in the data they've collected.

Still to come, there will be a joint, long-term Soviet-American study of the state of health of others who were living within eighteen miles of the Chernobyl reactor when it exploded. That study will be of interest to doctors from a number of countries, since, according to Dr. Gale, it will be able to compile a basis for a multifaceted collaboration in the area of the peaceful uses of atomic energy. Says Gale:

"I think the USSR acted wisely by inviting this group of foreign specialists here. Aside from the obvious advantages that medical collaborations bring to the patients, such a step helps establish trust between nations, trust in the questions of interpretation of what went on, the dimensions of the accident, and its real consequences. For example, the assessment that Dr. Blix, the General Director of the International Atomic Energy Commission, and I gave, coincided pretty exactly with the one that the Soviet specialists gave. And that's very important. In situations like this there can be a variety of areas of disagreement, and even misunderstanding."

Dr. A. Jammet, who also stopped in Kiev, came to the same conclusion, that it's important that the specialists' views be in basic agreement. Jammet is an extremely well-known specialist in the field of radiation protection and ecology, the president of the International Center of Radiopathology, and special advisor to the French Commissariat for Atomic Energy.

He says:

"I have known Madame Guskova for almost twenty years and I have never doubted her high degree of professionalism. The way she handled the treatment of the sick after the Chernobyl accident—the courage, the decisiveness, and the dynamism she has shown—has filled me with admiration.

"A second problem that takes on a special importance for me is the sanitary and public health aspects of the current condition of the stricken zone. It gives me pleasure to announce that the standard of practice to which the Soviet government adheres is analogous to the one adopted in France. And all the measures taken during the evacuation of the population, including, for example, the nutritional standards, generally correspond to those in our country.

"The experience of the Soviet Union in resolving the most complex problems associated with resettling people in new locations, decontaminating localities, and restoring the soil to an agriculturally usable condition has colossal significance, and when needed can be used by other governments."

One cannot but heed Professor Jammet's assessment. After all, he was the first doctor in the world to perform a bone-marrow transplant. His first patients, in the 1950s, were Yugoslav specialists who suffered radiation poisoning after an accident at a nuclear reactor in that country and were rushed to France. Most of those patients are still alive today, and one woman has even given birth to two children.

10

SUBDUING THE REACTOR:
How the Encasement Was Built
and Unit 4 Was "Entombed,"
May to October

I t was a day that had been awaited a long time—more than five months in all from that April night when people had caught sight of the destroyed building of Reactor No. 4, the black smoke of the Chernobyl Nuclear Power Plant. The scale of the catastrophe was not yet clear, nor the full dimensions of the tragedy; the understanding of all of that came later. There was still no work plan; plans were born and changed, though the work never ceased for a minute.

And now the "sarcophagus" over the crippled reactor had been erected.

There were no ready-made answers; the workers made decisions as they went along. If one approach didn't work, another was found. One thing was clear: the need to extinguish, get under control, and neutralize the volatile reactor. During the first stage helicopters protected by makeshift lead screens dropped isolating materials directly onto the source of deadly radiation. Only later did you start hearing the word *sarcophagus*. I shouted it (the connection was bad) over the telephone from Chernobyl in the middle of May while dictating a news story to *Izsvestiya*. Earlier I had heard about the "sarcophagus" from Mr. I. Silayev, head of the government commission set up to eliminate the effects of the accident.

Allow me a digression. I would like to explain a certain matter about which I've been asked many times to dispel some rumors and distortions.

In May, at a press conference for Soviet and foreign reporters, Mr. B. Scherbina, who holds the position of vice president of the Council of Ministers of the USSR, appeared. After the accident, he was appointed president of the Government Commission for Eliminating the After-effects of the Accident. This news was reported by radio, television, and newspaper. But why have I quoted others, namely, Mr. I. Silayev and Mr. Voronin, also vice presidents of the USSR Council of Ministers, referring to them as presidents of the Government Commission set up in Chernobyl?

The answer is simple. They change presidents. Having worked within the thirty-kilometer zone for a certain period of time (a time defined by doctors), each is replaced by someone else and then returned to Moscow. The person assigned to this difficult duty is someone of high governmental rank. It makes sense. Here in Chernobyl the types of decisions being made result in enormous cash expenditures, the rearrangement of trains, the rescheduling of airplanes, and the transfer of thousands of people from their homes. This enormous responsibility was borne by temporary presidents of the Government Commission for Eliminating the After-effects of the Accident at the atomic power plant. Needless to say, they live and work on the job alongside scientists and various specialists; they develop tactics and strategy concerning work at the reactor site together with them.

The concept of a "sarcophagus" soon became as much a part of everyone's vocabulary at the site as "radiation." When the sarcophagus was being sealed, the tensest stage in eliminating the effects of the accident was drawing to a close. What, from a technical point of view, was this twentieth-century sarcophagus? "It would be wrong to think," said Academician Velikhov, "that the sarcophagus is some sort of grave in which Reactor No. 4, together with its radioactive fuel, will be buried. That would be too easy. The sarcophagus is quite a complicated construction. To build it, designers were faced with problems no one has ever had to solve before."

During the course of the clean-up the concept of the sarcophagus gradually emerged as the best solution. Imagine the technical complexity: it was built right in the center of the most dangerous zone, and its structure rose 61 meters in height. Before a sarcophagus could be built, entire cement plants had to be set up, new roads had to be laid, and thousands of tons of metal framing had to be gathered. The project managers had to provide places to live and amenities for thousands of people, set up machine tool shops as good as those in any factory, and assure a steady and reliable dosimeter service.

Among the participants in the construction of the sarcophagus were the engineers, workers, and specialists of the Institute of Atomic Energy named after I. V. Kurchatov, the Institute for Atomic Research of the Ukrainian Academy of Sciences, and others.

The day of the "roof raising" was approaching. The date had already been set for giving the structure its "rafters." Covering these rafters with a layer of cement would stop the radiation leak. Still to come was an unprecedented engineering feat: lifting and placing at great height a frame made of steel beams weighing 165 tons.

Suddenly, a key assembly of the crane specially put together on site malfunctioned; the enormous load swayed, hanging in the air. The giant crane's jib was more than 70 meters tall; each of its caterpillar tracks weighed 82 tons. Now it was necessary to fix it. They had to delay putting on the roof for several days.

Now the big day came again. The steel beams were set in place. With the help of numerous television set-ups covering every possible view of the sarcophagus, the mounting was directed. The mechanism set up for releasing the lines from the load performed perfectly; the jib moved up and over—and it was on! Everyone in the project control office heaved a sigh of relief. People were sitting in a special structure the workers had dubbed "the bunker."

Commented A. Usanov, a member of the Government Commission:

"Starting in the first days of July, we began to fill the body of the sarcophagus with cement—about 5,700 cubic meters a day—about half a million cubic meters all told. No one had done work like this before. The difficulty was that every construction operation had to work correctly on the first try. Because of the intense radiation, no one could walk out onto the platform of this unusual structure. After the covering wall had been completed, the goal of blocking the deadly radiation escaping from Reactor No. 4 became a lot easier." ·

The rest depended on the skill of the crane operator, the coordination of tasks, and the precise fulfillment of orders sent by radio.

Cement, lead, and other special materials covered the damaged reactor securely; still, this was only a covering. The radioactive process within the reactor had not yet been stopped altogether; heat was still being produced. A myriad of instruments buried beneath the roof of the sarcophagus monitored the reactor. Excess heat was removed by technical systems, and a cooling system was also devised, providing the "lungs" of the structure. Within the block many meters of pipe 180 centimeters in diameter had been set up. Filters built into these "lungs" prevented radioactive dust from escaping beyond the walls of the sarcophagus.

As I walked towards the sarcophagus filled with fancy technology, a gray October drizzle was falling. Even as late as August such a stroll would have amounted to lunacy: the damaged reactor still had its approaches "lit up." Now its terrible "light" had been turned off by a solid containment building: a sarcophagus.

What now? The decision had been made to "reactivate" the Chernobyl Atomic Power Station. How would they manage the work at this and the other reactors?

Here is the commentary of Erik Pozdyshev, an experienced specialist. He has worked in the field of atomic energy for twenty-six years, more than half his life. In 1960 he finished Leningrad University with a degree in physics. He has worked at atomic energy plants in Leningrad, Kursk, and Smolensk. During the second half of May he was invited here to take over as the director of the atomic plant. Said Mr. Pozdyshev:

"It's true: the first and second reactors are to start operation by fall. The service personnel and those continuing the work of eliminating the effects of the accident will be working on the rotation system.

The energy workers and their families will receive apartments in Kiev. The on-duty period at the Chernobyl station will last approximately fifteen days. A base camp has been built for those on the active part of the rotation at Green Cape (Zelenyi Mys). After working fifteen days—a check-up and off to rest. Two weeks later you're back on the job. That will be the pattern for everyone, including me, the director."

Needless to say, the first and second units of the atomic power plant would be turned on only after upgrading them in accordance with the new safety guidelines for atomic energy devised by the Governmental Commission.

The heroes of the disaster were the firemen who were on the scene within minutes, pouring water on the flames. They were successful in preventing the other three nuclear reactors from catching fire and creating a holocaust.

Another group of heroes are the people who entered the stricken area to contain or dispel the radiation in Chernobyl.

It was up to others to explain to the world the scope of the accident, the successful evacuation of citizens in the area, and the after effects of a major nuclear disaster.

THOUGH THE OTHER THREE REACTORS AT THE CHERNOBYL
ATOMIC COMPLEX ARE NOT YET BACK IN OPERATION, WORK
ON THEM CONTINUES. HERE, SENIOR ENGINEER A.
BOCHAROV, WHO IS RESPONSIBLE FOR THE TURBINES, IS AT
MONITOR CONTROLS.

HELICOPTER, RIGHT, DECONTAMINATES TREES AND SHRUBS
AROUND THE FOURTH REACTOR.

FIREMAN LIEUTENANT VLADIMIR PRAVIK, ONE OF THE 28
YOUNG MEN FROM THE FIRE-STATION AT PRIPYAT. HIS
COMPANY, NO. 2, WAS THE FIRST TO ARRIVE ON THE SCENE.
HE ASSUMED COMMAND OF THE OPERATION.

LIEUTENANT VICTOR KIBENOK ARRIVED ON THE SITE FIVE
MINUTES AFTER PRAVIK.

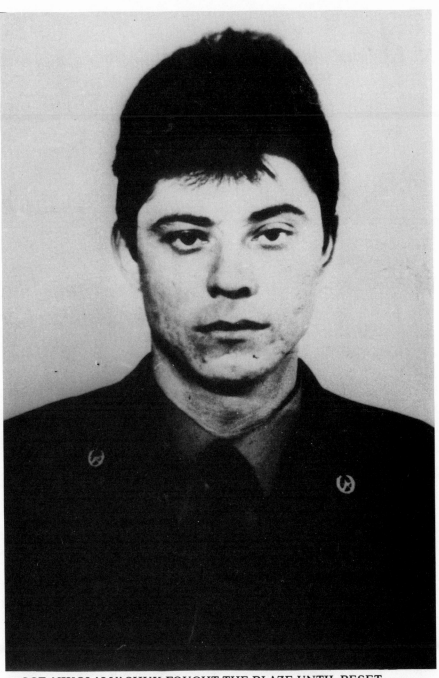

SGT. NIKOLAI VASHUK FOUGHT THE BLAZE UNTIL BESET
WITH EXHAUSTION. HE LOST CONSCIOUSNESS BECAUSE OF
SMOKE AND RADIATION AND HAD TO BE RESCUED.

SENIOR SGT. NIKOLAI TITENOK, WORK UNTIL HE WAS
OVERCOME BY HEAT AND RADIATION. HE COULD NOT GET
DOWN FROM THE ROOF ON HIS OWN.

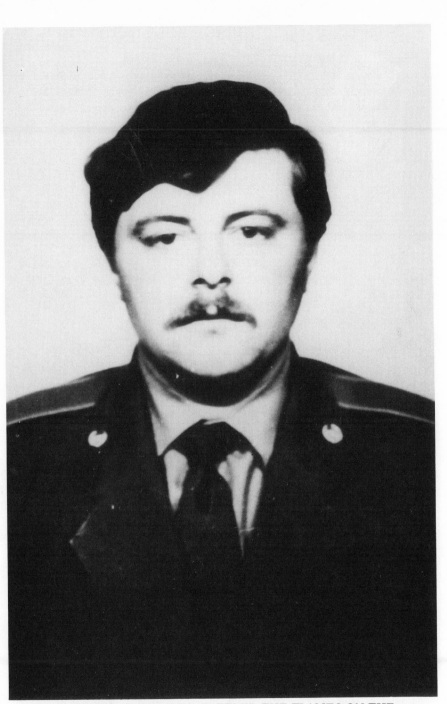

SGT. VLADIMIR TISHCHURA BATTLED THE FLAMES ON THE ROOF ABOVE THE CONTROL ROOM.

SENIOR SGT. VASILII IGNATENKO WAS ONE OF THE FIRST TO
REACH THE FIRE. HIS COMPANY CUT OFF THE PATH OF THE
FIRE FROM THE THREE UNDAMAGED REACTORS. HE STAYED
UNTIL THE FIRE WAS OUT.

SPECIALLY EQUIPPED HELICOPTERS SPRAYING TREES NEAR
THE PLANT.

A COLUMN OF SPECIAL CONTAINER TRUCKS CARRYING LIQUID
DECONTAMINANTS MOVING TOWARDS CHERNOBYL.

THE CHELYABINSK TRACTOR, WHICH CAN BE OPERATED BY REMOTE CONTROL, IS SHOWN HERE BEING TESTED.

CLOSE COOPERATION BETWEEN THE PILOTS OF THE KIEV
UNIFIED AIR COMMAND AND SCIENTISTS OF THE INSTITUTE
OF PHYSICAL-ORGANIC CHEMISTRY, AND COAL CHEMISTRY OF
THE ACADEMY OF SCIENCES, UKRAINE USSR, HELPED
DECONTAMINATE THE FORESTS AND FIELDS.

CONSTANT CHECKING FOR RADIATION IS A MUST.

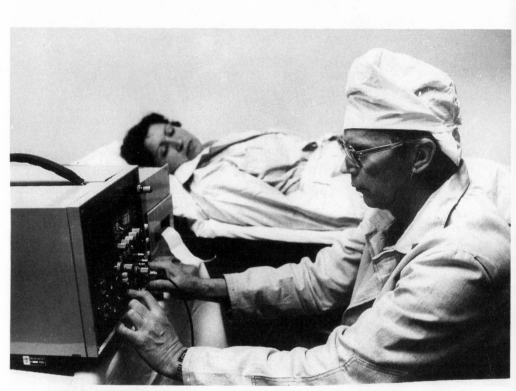

LAB WORKER, ZINAIDA KRASNOZHEN, IS EXAMINED BY
VITALY PERMINOV, HEAD OF THE SPECTROMETRY
LABORATORY.

GROUP OF SANITATION VOLUNTEERS FROM THE "PEREMOG" COLLECTIVE FARM OF THE BORODYANSK REGION, SET UP PREVENTIVE MEASURES AGAINST RADIATION CONTAMINATION.

TWO WEEKS AFTER THE ACCIDENT, CORRESPONDENTS OF A
WEST GERMAN TV STATION FILMED THE RADIATION CONTROL
OF WATER AT ONE OF THE LAKES IN THE MAKAROVSK REGION
OF KIEV DISTRICT.

ON MAY 9, 1986, FOREIGN JOURNALISTS INTERVIEWED
EVACUEES FROM WITHIN THE 30-MILE ZONE. FOREGROUND,
LIDIA NERUS WHO CAME FROM THE VILLAGE OF OPACHICHI IN
THE CHERNOBYL REGION.

MAY 9, 1986, FOREIGN JOURNALISTS MUST PASS THROUGH A
DOSIMETER CHECKPOINT IN THE VILLAGE OF KOPYLOV.

PARTICIPANTS IN THE CHERNOBYL CLEAN—UP ARE HUNGRY
FOR NEWS AS WELL AS WANTING TO CHECK THE PULSE OF
THEIR OWN COUNTRY AND THE REST OF THE WORLD.

VLADIMIR KRIVENKO (LEFT), TALKS WITH THE SHIFT
FOREMAN AT THE FIRST REACTOR BUILDING AT THE
CHERNOBYL COMPLEX, DMITRII OVCHARENKO. DISCUSSION
WAS ABOUT FAMILIES AND FRIENDS.

FAMED SOVIET SINGER JOSEPH KOBZON VISITED CHERNOBYL
AND GAVE A CONCERT FOR THE WORKERS.

ON MAY 21, 1986, IN KIEV, THE PRESIDENT OF THE UKRANIAN
COUNCIL OF MINISTERS, ALEXANDER LYASHKO, RECEIVED
THE HEADS OF DIPLOMATIC LEGATIONS WHO WERE INVITED
TO THE UKRAINE FOR A PROGRESS REPORT ON THE
CHERNOBYL.

THE HEADS OF LEGATIONS IN ATTENDANCE AT THE MAY 21,
1986 MEETING WITH ALEXANDER LYASHKO.

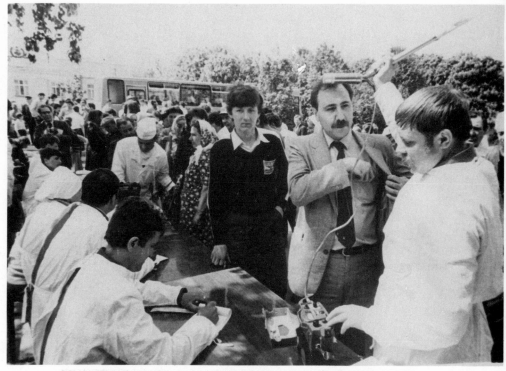

MUSAFIR SALYAM, A CORRESPONDENT FOR THE KUWAIT
NEWSPAPER "AL-AIBA" JUMPED INTO THE EVACUEE LINE THAT
WAS PASSING THROUGH THE DOSIMETER CONTROL. HE
WANTED TO CONVINCE HIMSELF OF THE ABSENCE OF
RADIATION.

SENIOR MACHINE OPERATOR VLADIMIR IVOKHIN AND SENIOR
ENGINEER MICHAEL POKHODEN TAKING A STROLL NEAR IN
"FOREST GLADE" A HEALTH AND REST AREA NEAR KIEV.

ALEXANDER KOLGIN, A SENIOR MACHINE OPERATOR AT THE
SHOP OF REACTOR NO. 2, PLAYS THE PIANO FOR HIS FRIENDS.

CHILDREN WHO WERE EVACUATED FROM CHERNOBYL, NOW
LIVING IN A HEALTH-CARE SANITARIUM WHILE THEIR
PARENTS WORK ON THE CLEAN-UP.

CHILDREN OF CHERNOBYL WORKERS AT A SUMMER CAMP.

THE GORKAVY FAMILY IN THE VILLAGE OF KOLOSHIN (NEAR
KIEV) TOOK IN SIX PEOPLE WHO WERE EVACUATED FROM
CHERNOBYL.

РАСТЕТ СЕЛО

A NEW VILLAGE OF 240 FARM HOUSES BEING BUILT NEAR LUKYANOVKA FOR PEOPLE EVACUATED FROM THE 30-MILE ZONE.

A STUDENT CONSTRUCTION TEAM, FROM THE KIEV GOVERNMENTAL PEDAGOGICAL INSTITUTE, AND CALLING THEMSELVES "HELIOS" CAME TO HELP BUILD A NEW VILLAGE FOR EVACUEES.

11

WHAT THE CHERNOBYL ACCIDENT TAUGHT THE USSR, AND WHAT IT HAS TO TEACH THE WORLD?

The accident at the Chernobyl power station shocked our entire nation. Chernobyl is a tragedy that forced us to look at many things in a new way. It was a hard blow, first, because of the loss of life and the pain of the victims' relatives and loved ones. Almost 100,000 people in the Ukraine area were uprooted from their homes. Then there was the damage to nature and the economy. It was a blow to a simple concept, one familiar not only to our country, but to dozens of other countries as well: the concept of the peaceful atom to help turn turbines at electric stations, a new way to create energy. Finally, significant financial losses were suffered by the government. Taken all together, these problems and disappointments amounted to a need for the most serious stock taking.

The highest government and Party organs in the nation took a long, hard look at the events that had worried millions of people since the spring of this year. The specific people on whom the blame rests for the explosion at the fourth reactor at Chernobyl will stand trial. The prosecutor's office is making an extremely detailed inquiry into every step, every order, every decision made by every person involved that could have contributed to the eventual disaster.

Unquestionably, the accident was caused by workers who violated a whole series of rules regulating the use of reactor equipment. The very night the reactor was being shut down for scheduled repairs, experiments designed to test turbines were taking place. At the same time, the directors and technical specialists at the reactor failed to prepare adequately for such a complicated operation. They failed to coordinate it with the other organizations involved, although operational procedures require that this be done. They did not ensure supervision of the experiment and did not use all available safety measures. The consequences of such irresponsibility and lack of discipline were disastrous: death and disease for some, monstrous risk for others, the fire that destroyed the reactor, and the radioactive contamination of the territory surrounding the station, about a thousand square kilometers. A number of directors have been dismissed from their duties.

Everyone who works in the field of atomic energy—from ministries and departments to scientific and engineering organizations to economic, Soviet, and Party organs—will have to follow new guidelines and exercise a new vigilance.

In the shortest possible period (these activities are already well under way) new methods are being developed and executed to add further safety measures in the use of active atomic electrical power generators, to strengthen technical discipline, and to upgrade observation of regulations established for the operation of reactors and other equipment. Simultaneously, service personnel are going through retraining and recertification; the network of technical training centers equipped with simulators is growing. Government supervisory agencies have been charged with strict supervision of all atomic power stations.

A new ministry—the Ministry of Atomic Energy—has been created in order to improve management of atomic energy development and to promote a responsible attitude toward work in the industry.

The use of atomic energy is a contemporary fact of life. Atomic energy came onto the stage in the modern era not, however, through an act of creation, but through an act of war and the destruction of hundreds of thousands of lives. Between the first atomic pile created by Enrico Fermi and the first industrial atomic power station started by Igor Kurchatov lie the shadows of Hiroshima and Nagasaki.

Today, nuclear stockpiles have reached dimensions threatening the existence of life on Earth. The time has come to realize that the preservation of human civilization is the responsibility of all governments, because nuclear war would ineluctably touch all of us. It is not too late to put an end to this suicidal course toward a catastrophic confrontation, starting instead a realistic program for disarmament.

It is true that the "peaceful" atom hides within itself significant dangers. This has been demonstrated by the various accidents at nuclear plants. It is why all countries must work together to ensure that there is zero possibility of an accident occurring at a nuclear installation. Wherever nuclear plants already exist—in the USSR, the United States, France, Sweden, and so on—or where they soon will exist, must ensure complete safety of operation. We are faced with two interrelated tasks: ensuring the safety of peaceful uses of the atom and freeing the planet from nuclear weapons. Both tasks require the broad cooperation and joint efforts of governments and international organizations, of nuclear organizations especially, and of all social forces concerned with the creation of an all-embracing and secure system of international safety. For this to happen every country must act independently as well as cooperatively towards these ends.

In his televised speech concerning the nuclear accident, Mikhail Gorbachev stated:

"In our view, the accident at Chernobyl, like the accidents at American, English, and other atomic power stations, confront each and every government with extremely serious questions which demand responsible consideration.

"Today throughout the world more than 370 atomic reactors are functioning. This is the reality. It is hard to imagine the future of the world economy without atomic energy. In our country today forty reactors are operating with a combined output exceeding 28 million kilowatts. We all know that the peaceful atom brings many benefits to mankind.

"Clearly, though, we are obliged to act still more cautiously, and we must concentrate all our scientific and technical efforts on ensuring the safe exploitation of the great and threatening forces held within the atomic nucleus.

"For us, the indisputable lesson of Chernobyl lies in this: the principles regulating the further development of the scientific-techno-logical revolution must be safety, discipline, order, and organization. Everywhere and in all respects we must operate according to the strictest standards.

"Furthermore, we consider it essential to work for a significant increase in intergovernmental cooperation within the framework of the International Atomic Energy Agency."

What does the USSR propose to do to ensure that the Chernobyl tragedy becomes the last entry where nuclear energy slips out of control? First, let me cite a few figures. I think it makes sense to repeat a few of the figures mentioned earlier, since these present the concrete reality of twentieth-century life.

At present 370 atomic reactors are operating throughout the world. It is estimated that by the year 2000 nuclear energy will account for more than 20 percent of global energy output. In several countries nuclear-generated power accounts for more than 50 percent of their electrical power production. Thirty-plus years of experience with atomic electrical power generators has shown convincingly that they can be a viable, economical, and ecologically clean form of energy production.

In recent years the geographic distribution of nuclear energy has grown significantly. A number of developing countries in Asia, Latin America, and Africa are building or have already built atomic power stations or reactors used in research. The time has come to speed up work on developing and putting into production controlled thermonuclear reactors, which could someday become the source of inexhaustible energy. Since 1978, on the initiative of the Soviet Union, Soviet, West European, American, and Japanese scientists stationed in Vienna have been developing a project for the construction of an international experimental thermonuclear reactor. Such a reactor would be in the interests of the vast majority of countries vitally interested in new forms of energy. And what is especially significant, this direction of research has no military applications.

What if this latest twist of scientific thought should lead to dangers even greater than Chernobyl? The fear is unfounded, say the specialists: thermonuclear energy, of all the forms of power generation, will prove the least harmful to the environment. One can already state with confidence that the construction of such a reactor in the near future is technically feasible.

The peaceful atom will allow us to satisfy humanity's ever-growing demands for energy to fuel industry, agriculture, and scientific research. Today there is no alternative energy source that can take its place.

The world has experienced more than 150 accidents involving atomic power plants that resulted in leakage of radiation. Some of these accidents—in the United States, West Germany, England, Yugoslavia, and, finally, Chernobyl—have had serious consequences, including economic and psychological damage. The planet Earth is small: this too is a truth of the twentieth century. Events of this sort can affect neighboring countries as well. This demonstrates the interdependence of all countries. The realities of the nuclear and cosmic era require that all peoples come to think of themselves as a single family on the planet Earth.

The lesson learned by the Soviet Union from the accident at Chernobyl power station can be summed up briefly: development of nuclear power must take place in conditions maximally providing for the safety of humans and the natural environment. The accident showed how important far-reaching international cooperation is for achieving nuclear safety in the full sense of the word.

Now let me state the policy conclusions the Soviet Union has drawn from the above.

As soon as possible an effective system must be set up for notification about accidents and malfunctions at atomic power plants where leakage of radiation carries the risk of crossing a country's borders. The goal is to reduce the consequences to other countries by allowing them to take precautionary measures for the safety of the population and the environment.

Such a system could be significantly improved by making accessible to all an information bank on radiation levels at specific geographic locales. National institutes could collect the data and transmit them to a single international center.

As many countries do not have the resources to deal with a

nuclear accident, the Soviet Union calls for the creation of a response force capable of coming to the assistance of a country in a dangerous situation. Such a mechanism would form an integral part of the new international energy-safety system.

It is also quite important that all countries follow the standards set by the International Atomic Energy Agency for the safe operation of nuclear installations. These recommendations might embrace such matters as choice of reactor site, design, construction, deployment, retirement from use, and the disposal of radioactive wastes.

The competent development of nuclear energy would be greatly facilitated by the collection, processing, and exchange of information about nuclear accidents, the reasons for their occurrence, and the nature and consequences of the malfunction. The USSR has taken the first step by giving the International Atomic Energy Agency detailed information about the reasons, course, and consequences of the accident at Chernobyl.

Another important way in which the combined forces of different countries could improve the safety picture in atomic energy would be to collaborate in the design of a new generation of nuclear reactors, whether of the thermal-neutron or the fast-neutron type.

These proposals relate to nuclear safety in normal situations. But we live in a nonnormal, tumultuous world, so we must act with caution. Accidents can occur for reasons other than design flaws or irresponsible actions during the operation of the reactor. For example, the intentional destruction of atomic power stations or research reactors could release radioactive substances into the environment. Even conventional weapons, if used to destroy a peaceful atomic installation, would take on the character of nuclear weapons. The attack would be what the United Nations has described as a crime against humanity.

For this reason the Soviet Union has proposed the development of a system for preventing attacks on nuclear installations. Guarantees must be obtained from all nations against the attacking of nuclear installations.

Nuclear terrorism—the words alone, to say nothing of the act, give rise to the profoundest anxieties. Moreover, intentional attacks on atomic industrial centers have already taken place, as has the theft of highly enriched fissionable materials. Because of the dangers of radioactivity, nuclear materials must be securely defended against any encroachment.

If you follow this chain of logic—the materials were stolen; therefore, someone needed them—you cannot exclude the possibility that stolen materials might be used for the creation of a crude nuclear device. An atom bomb in the hands of a terrorist would present a frightful danger. The time has come to work out a well-thought-out antinuclear-terrorism system. Our country is ready and willing to reach agreements in this area.

All of the above proposals have already been set before international bodies by our country's specialists and are presently being discussed and analyzed by those concerned. These discussions touch on many other technical and legal questions. These problems must be resolved. Mankind today stands face to face with the following choice: either to rush into an arms race and face the abyss of nuclear self-destruction or, the more desirable choice, to face the realities of the nuclear age.

■ ■ ■

In the course of gathering material about Chernobyl, I met hundreds of people of diverse ages and life experiences. Many of their thoughts have appeared on these pages. Quite possibly, some of these judgments contradict each other; not all the people I interviewed share my views. This is not surprising, since no two people are the same. When it comes to matters of critical importance, perhaps no two opinions are the same either.

In one respect, however, everyone I met with, or quoted, or whose statements I heard or read about, or with whom I argued, was united. Every last one of them. Not one of them was indifferent about the tragedy at Chernobyl. Some were frightened, some were furious, some doubted whether atomic energy was capable of being of value to humanity. They treated the event with the utmost serious concern: yes, the accident obliges us to reflect on our actions, to be stricter with ourselves, to become more professional on the job, but I believe that in no way should it hinder the development of nuclear energy.

Perhaps it's best to conclude with the following words of

the Swedish director of the International Atomic Energy Agency, Hans Bliks:

"Our generation understands that it is not the world that belongs to us, but we who belong to the world. We must hand on to future generations a clean planet. Hence the efforts of all governments must be focused on the destruction of nuclear weapons and on minimizing the risks of the use of nuclear energy."

Under such words such as these I put my signature as well.

IN PLACE OF AN EPILOGUE
Pushkin Square.
The Most Frequently Asked Questions

Pushkin Square lies at the very center of Moscow; 5 Pushkin Street is the address of the newspaper *Izsvestiya*. "Pushkin Square" also happens to be the name of the paper's column dedicated to the comments of passersby on diverse—but always timely—matters.

This spot was chosen as a way to sound out public opinion, not because it lies a stone's throw from the paper's editorial offices. No. This is the center of an enormous city visited daily by countless visitors. Hence, by conducting spot interviews here, one can learn the opinions of people living in all parts of the Soviet Union and from all corners of the globe.

I embarked on a bit of research in hopes of finding out people's concerns regarding the accident at Chernobyl. Gathering the numerous answers together for comparison, I have managed, I hope, to get a sense of which questions about Chernobyl are still somewhat foggy in people's minds and which questions people have been unable to answer on their own.

As it turned out, most of these questions required information that only experts could provide. Answers to the most burning questions on people's minds have been included in this book. I used them for this purpose to probe the opinions of leading authorities from various fields. I hope these questions and answers will help the reader understand the consequences of the Chernobyl tragedy and learn at first hand the latest and most precise account of what happened.

■ ■ ■

Q. How does a reactor of the Chernobyl type work?

A. To answer the question about the functioning of a million-kilowatt reactor I called upon Boris Semenov, vice president of the USSR Committee on the Use of Atomic Energy.

Uranium-graphite reactors of the type used at Chernobyl have a long history in our country. The first atomic energy installation ever built, the one built thirty years ago in the city of Obninsk, just outside of Moscow, was a reactor of this type.

The same construction principles were used in the design of the Beloyarskaya atomic energy station. After many successful years of operation, the next step was taken: the construction of a series of powerful stations. The first such RBMK-1000 (the initials stand for Canal Reactor of Large Output) went on line in Leningrad in 1973. Experts had no complaints about either this reactor or those that followed it. All such reactors have given long years of faithful and reliable service.

Now for some technical details. The electric output of the atomic energy installation is 1,000 megawatts. The thermal energy produced by the reactor is much greater: 3,200 megawatts. The reactor is cooled with boiling water through the so-called single-contour system.

Uranium dioxide of low concentration serves as the fuel. It contains approximately 20 kilograms of nuclear fuel per ton. The normal load of fuel is 180 tons. Graphite is used to moderate the nuclear reaction. The temperature of the steam before it comes in contact with the turbines reaches 280 degrees while at 65 atmospheres.*

People often ask why the Chernobyl-type reactor doesn't make use of the more traditional thick-walled reactor vessel, which is capable of withstanding high pressure. Wouldn't this result in greater safety?

It is true that the RBMK-1000 type reactor does not have

*An atmosphere is a unit of pressure.

such a vessel. The graphite bricks are held within a thin-walled hermetic casing. The fuel assemblies are located inside cladding made of zirconium alloy. And it is these that hold the pressure of the water. It is precisely this sort of channel reactor that is safest. The thick-walled vessel under high pressure is, from the point of view of safety, the least reliable.

The design of the RBMK-1000 takes into account the possibility of a breakdown situation: there is a special emergency system for cooling the active zone. In order to prevent the escape of steam and fission products in case of a breach, the primary reactor equipment is housed in sturdy compartments designed to withstand a surplus pressure of 4.5 atmospheres. Under the accident scenarios contemplated by the designers, any discharges would have been localized here, and steam would have accumulated in a special pool.

■ ■ ■

Q. Why wasn't information about the accident released immediately after it happened?

A. "This was our first experience with an accident of this kind; I won't deny that I had no idea of the true dimensions of the accident," answered Academician Valery Legasov, deputy director of the Institute of Atomic Energy named after I. Kurchatov. "We learned of the fact of an accident immediately, but the information coming from Chernobyl contained many contradictions. To immediately understand and evaluate what had happened just wasn't possible.

"On the morning of the twenty-sixth of April a group of experts and a government commission, of which I was a member, flew to Chernobyl for a first look at what had happened. Only as we were driving up to the city of Pripyat, from which I could see the glow of the flames, did I begin to realize the dimensions of the accident. As someone who participated in the clean-up work at the accident, I knew it was simply impossible to evaluate the situation accurately from Moscow. As a specialist and participant in these events, I can tell you with assurance that the chances of the accident being of this dimension seemed improbable, almost fantastic. There was no dark motive, no desire to hide anything."

■ ■ ■

Q. Who specifically is guilty for the accident?

A. No complete answer to this question will be possible until the investigative work is completed and the degree of guilt of all those involved in the accident is determined. One can only say today that the directors of the power plant committed serious mistakes. Bryukhanov, the former director of the nuclear power plant, and Fomin, the chief engineer, proved unable to ensure proper management of the nuclear power station, and showed indecision and irresponsibility at the moment of the accident and afterwards. They did not manage to evaluate properly what was taking place and failed to take urgent countermeasures. Because of their inability to organize work and take upon themselves the responsibility for the safety of the workers at the power station and their families, a portion of the plant's workers left the city. This complicated the situation in the first days after the accident, since among those who had left their posts had been a number of foremen and senior technicians.

A list of those individuals facing severe punishments (including directors of institutes and administrators at ministries) has been published in the Soviet press.

■ ■ ■

Q. Did radioactive materials continue to enter the atmosphere after the twenty-sixth of April?

A. "Radioactive materials were ejected into the atmosphere only at the time of the accident and for the first few days afterwards. The nuclear reaction as such stopped immediately and did not resume. Beyond this one can only refer to the remaining, small heat-discharge given off by the nuclear fuel," answers Academician Evgenii Velikhov, vice president of the Academy of Sciences of the USSR.

In his talks published in press, Academician Velikhov, who was among the first people to arrive at the site of the accident, stated: "Having almost touched with my bare hands the danger contained within the atom, I feel more strongly than ever the necessity of struggling for the liquidation of nuclear weapons.

The world's nuclear arsenals hold today more than fifty thousand warheads. Figuratively speaking, every man, woman, and child on planet Earth is sitting on a barrel containing three tons of explosives. The energy contained in each of these symbolic barrels is sufficient to send every person on a trip into space."

Or, I would add, on a voyage of no return.

■ ■ ■

Q. Why wasn't the population in the area of the accident evacuated immediately?

A. "There's an old Russian saying: 'Before you throw yourself into the well, you should check the church calendar,' " answers Boris Semenov, vice president of the USSR Governmental Committee on the Use of Atomic Energy. "First we had to evaluate and understand the true nature of the accident. As soon as this was clear, preparations for the evacuation got under way. Here you're talking about evacuating tens of thousands of people during peacetime on a Sunday. To organize and prepare for all of this required a certain amount of time.

■ ■ ■

Q. What was the total number of people evacuated?

A. The number of people evacuated from the thirty-kilometer zone in the Ukraine came to some ninety-three thousand. When a portion of these people returned to those regions where there was no radiation danger, this number fell to 89,460 persons.

■ ■ ■

Q. Where and in what living conditions are those people who left their homes?

A. On the construction of farmhouses in the Ukraine and White Russia 300 million rubles have been allocated. Almost eleven thousand such homes have been constructed, with each home valued at an average of thirty thousand rubles. In the Ukraine alone more than fifty new villages have been built for the evacuees. For the workers at the power station and those living in Pripyat, seventy-five hundred Kiev apartments have been assigned and five hundred apartments in Chernigov. Ten thousand places in dormitories have been made available as temporary housing. In the Kiev region, six thousand homes were bought from the local population and transferred free of charge to evacuees.

■ ■ ■

Q. How were people compensated for the loss of property?

A. Five hundred million rubles were allocated from the government's budget to help those who suffered damages, of which 100 million rubles came out of social insurance. The average salary is being paid to those who have temporarily lost the ability to work. Grants-in-aid are being paid. Farmers are being compensated for the loss of their crops. Apartments and homes are being provided free of charge. Large, interest-free loans with a repayment schedule of fifteen years are being made available.

The average compensation disbursed to each household in, for example, White Russia amounted to more than fourteen thousand rubles. One-time grants-in-aid totaled almost fifteen million rubles. All expenditures of the first days after the accident for food, clothes, and bedding were absorbed by the collective farms that took in the evacuees.

■ ■ ■

Q. What is the "Account No. 904"?

A. This is the name of the account opened by Gosbank (the government bank) for receiving aid funds brought in voluntarily by Soviet citizens and organizations, as well as by residents of other countries. In the month of June alone this account took in 300 million rubles. By the beginning of October the account held more than 500 million rubles. Foreigners as well as Soviet citizens residing abroad contributed the equivalent of 1.5 million rubles in foreign currency.

Every resident of the USSR voluntarily contributed one day's labor without pay. The day's salary for this day of work was transferred to the fund used to help those who suffered from the accident.

■ ■ ■

Q. Were not other countries justified in their decisions to limit or even forbid the import of agricultural products from the USSR?

A. Agricultural products contaminated with radiation are not the same thing as products with potassium cyanide inside them. It is quite easy to detect the presence of radiation: every customs point has the necessary apparatus. "The problem clearly wasn't the danger of food products from our country," says Professor A. Vorobyov, Soviet radiology specialist. "It was a political decision and not one based on a real danger."

■ ■ ■

Q. Was it dangerous to spend the summer on the Black Sea?

A. For an answer to this question you might turn to the Swedish filmmakers who participated in a joint Soviet-Swedish film production based on the stories of Astrid Lindgren. After arriving in the Crimea, they immediately set about testing out the water, air, cherries, flowers, etc., with their instruments, and then called down to Yalta for their wives and children.

■ ■ ■

Q. What safety measures were taken in Kiev where the background radiation was at a higher level?

A. Ukrainian minister of health Romanenko appeared there on television many times. Among the basic preventative measures he recommended, first of all, household sanitation: daily cleaning of the house with water, wet sponges, etc. It was recommended that homes be aired out after it rained, when there was no wind or dust. People were told to shower and shampoo their hair daily. The minister thought it best not to allow children to play outdoors all day long, especially if it meant playing games such as soccer on dusty lots. Since keeping children indoors all day, especially in summertime, is a rather cruel thing to do, classes in Kiev were dismissed for grades 1 through 7 until the fifteenth of May and children were sent to recreational camps.

As the radiation picture changed, so changed also the suggestions from physicians. Later, when the background radiation was reduced, the health minister rescinded the recommendations closing windows, not taking walks, and not playing sports out of doors. Farmers working in the fields over the summer were asked to take their meals in places protected from wind and dust and to carry their water in closed containers. On numerous occasions the minister warned people against using home remedies, but despite all his efforts the abuse of medicaments, particularly of iodine preparations, led to a number of poisonings and burns in the esophagus.

■ ■ ■

Q. Wasn't there a danger of spreading radioactive dust carried on the tires of cars leaving the thirty-kilometer zone?

A. Theoretically, such a danger existed. Hence, at the points of entry to all population centers up to and including Moscow, check stations were set up. All transport was subject to verification by workers with dosimeters. Later, in order to reduce the risk of contamination to trucks, exchange points were set up on the perimeter of the thirty-kilometer zone where loads were transferred to and from "clean" trucks onto those working within the territory affected by radiation.

■ ■ ■

Q. What is radiation sickness?

A. To answer this question I would like to make use of the words of Yaroslav Golovanov, the well-known journalist and author who gave a talk on this very subject in connection with the events in Chernobyl.

"Radiation sickness is the reaction of a living organism to irradiation. But it would also be true to say that as many living organisms as there are, there are as many different reactions to irradiation. When scientists first began to study the effects of radiation on animals in laboratories, they quickly discovered a certain consistency: the more complex the organism, the more it was subject to radiation sickness. It's logical: a microscope is easier to break than an axe. It is also obvious that the larger the dose received, the more likely the onset of radiation sickness.

"But not everything is so straightforward, because radiation sickness is a multifaceted reaction of the entire body: the body responds not only to the total quantity of damaging rays of energy received, but also according to the manner in which the energy was received, the sort of radiant energy it was, the parts of the body and organs hit, and how the dose was received—little by little or all at once.

"A radioactive isotope that gets into a human body and damages the bone marrow—the main blood-producing organ—can bring about radiation sickness. Again one must ask: which isotope was it? It's difficult to calculate, for example, how much plutonium you would have to swallow in order to come down with radiation sickness. At any rate, it would have been a lot, probably something like a million rubles' worth. But if you take strontium-90 it doesn't take much at all.

"You can use the page of a newspaper to protect yourself from a stream of alpha rays, but if they get inside the body, they will literally turn any living tissue into ruins. This too is a form of radiation sickness. It's easy to see that, since all of these influences can occur in a variety of combinations, efforts to combat their effects are complex.

"Among higher organisms, man's sensitivity to radiation is moderate, occupying a place not far from that of dogs and monkeys. Yet there are cases where, as a result of accidents in laboratories, scientists have received exposure to levels of radiation significantly exceeding fatal doses and survived. Just as people vary in their ability to tolerate heat and sunlight—in other words, exposure to infrared or ultraviolet rays—so people also vary in their ability to tolerate radiation. The physical organism's resistance in such cases is individual, in the same way that the response is individual to infectious diseases; the mechanism of resistance is different. Much depends on a person's age, overall health, and ruggedness, even on the condition of his nervous system and mood! Any doctor will tell you that a person who delights in being alive is better able to tolerate illness. This applies as well to illnesses involving radiation."

■ ■ ■

Q. How many people died as a result of the accident?

A. Thirty-one people were killed. Of these, six were firemen, one was a worker who was killed instantly at the moment of the accident, and another died several hours later from burns. The remaining victims were also workers at the reactor site.

■ ■ ■

Q. How many people were hospitalized?

A. Only 300 people. Of these, 203 were diagnosed with severe cases of radiation sickness of varying degrees of severity. Of the 300, 129 were sent in three airplanes to the Moscow clinic on April 27. These were the severest cases, in need of especially complex forms of medical assistance.

■ ■ ■

Q. Were there any casualties among the populations of nearby cities and villages?

A. A painstaking analysis of several hundred people found not one single case of radiation sickness.

■ ■ ■

Q. Could the accident at Chernobyl bring about cases of radiation sickness in other countries?

A. This is the view of Dr. Jammet, president of the International Center for Radiopathology:

"This is impossible. According to the calculations of specialists, the largest dose of radiation that could be received by persons residing in the European countries would not exceed the dose of cosmic radiation received by someone flying round-trip between Paris and Los Angeles. Since the government of France does not forbid such flights, it would be unreasonable to take special precautions, or to expect serious consequences of any kind."

■ ■ ■

Q. Who were given medical checkups after the accident, and how were examinations performed?

A. All residents of Pripyat, Chernobyl, and all the villages lying within the thirty-kilometer zone were subject to compulsory medical examinations.

By decision of the Ministry of Health, tests for radiation were performed on anyone who asked for them. Not only in Kiev, but also in Moscow, special hospitals were assigned specifically to deal with this task. Doctors understood that even though the exposure to radiation may have been small, the psychological damage and stress suffered by those who were evacuated influenced not only their mood, but their health as well.

■ ■ ■

Q. How will continuing observation of those exposed to radiation be organized?

A. A center for medical radiology has been set up in Kiev. It has three separate departments: clinical epidemiology, clinics, and experimental radiology. A specialized six-hundred-bed hospital has been built, along with laboratory buildings. An information storage system has been set up with data about the location of every individual at the moment of the accident and afterwards. Those who underwent treatment in Moscow or Kiev have been entered into a special register. They will undergo a special system of long-term observation. Simultaneously with all this, new and effective preparations are being developed that block the accumulation of hazardous radioactive elements in body tissues.

■ ■ ■

Q. Wouldn't it be wiser to cease the development of atomic energy altogether if there is a risk of accidents of this sort?

A. "Personally, I am convinced that atomic stations represent the highest achievement of the energy industry. It lays the foundation for the next stage in the development of human civilization. What do I mean by this? It is not only that atomic power sources are more advantageous than thermal power stations from the economic standpoint; they are also cleaner from the ecological standpoint. Perhaps even more important, they set the stage for the next leap in technology. The future of civilization is unimaginable without atomic energy."

So states Academician Valery Legasov.

It is at the same time true that accidents at atomic power stations are harder to deal with than accidents at other types of power stations. The reason for this is clear: it is particularly difficult to liquidate the consequences of such accidents. What happened at Chernobyl had been considered improbable. The lessons to be drawn from it are technical, organizational, and psychological. What's more, these lessons are important not only for us, but for other countries as well.

■ ■ ■

Q. How many accidents occurred at atomic electric power stations prior to Chernobyl?

A. Between 1971 and 1984, 151 accidents occurred at atomic electric power stations in some fourteen countries. The word *accident* refers here to an event resulting in a significant release of radioactive material or injury to humans from such materials. This number of accidents bears witness to the reality that global standards of atomic energy usage are still far from perfect. In the opinion of experts, this very fact gives the lie to those who would accuse the Soviet atomic power industry of technical backwardness in comparison with other nations.

The most serious of these 151 accidents occurred at the American atomic plant at Three Mile Island in Pennsylvania. At 4 A.M. on the twenty-eighth of March 1979, the cooling system at Reactor No. 2 broke down and hydrogen that could have exploded at any moment began to accumulate. Only three days later did it become clear that the directors of the power station had consciously decided to release radioactive gases into the atmosphere without informing either local or federal authorities. On the twenty-ninth of March about 1.4 million liters of radioactively contaminated water was spilled into the Saskatchewan River.

Radiation levels in the surrounding area began to be checked only four days later. It proved impossible to avoid panic. It took ten days for information to reach Congress about what had happened; other countries learned about the accident after two months.

■ ■ ■

Q. How much energy will we have to forgo if we renounce the use of atomic energy?

A. The USSR started its first atomic power station in 1954. By the beginning of 1986 there were 370 atomic power stations operating throughout the world. Their combined electric output totals over 250 million kilowatts. In some countries atomic power plays a leading role in energy production. In Bulgaria, atomic power accounts for 30 percent of all energy production; in Switzerland, 35 percent; in Sweden, 39 percent; in Belgium, 50 percent; and in France, 65 percent.

By the year 2000, it is projected that atomic energy will provide approximately 20 percent of world energy production. In some countries this percentage will be much higher.

■　■　■

Q. Wouldn't it make more sense to build atomic power stations in unpopulated areas or in deserts?

A. To respond to this question I called upon Mr. Andranik Petrosyants, president of the USSR Government Committee on the Use of Atomic Energy:

"This is a very serious question and, in light of recent events, will evidently be answered in a new fashion. But to follow this advice and build atomic power stations in deserts will not be an easy thing to do.

"In deciding on a construction site for an atomic power plant one has to take into consideration a number of factors; for example, local seismic activity, the presence of sufficient quantities of water, roads, and services for the plant's personnel and their families. It takes about 1,000 people to staff a single reactor. This figure must be tripled if you include the families of those who provide services. Furthermore, we also must keep in mind the optimal distance for exploitation of a reactor: for every thousand kilometers of electric transmission by power lines you lose up to 10 percent of the original energy.

"Remember also that by no means do all countries have the same territorial resources as the Soviet Union. Most European countries are densely populated.

"Nonetheless, our country has drawn very serious conclusions from Chernobyl and these also touch on the question of where to locate atomic power stations. New norms and requirements in this regard are already being drawn up."

■　■　■

Q. What is "Tokamak"?

A. The future of atomic energy lies in harnessing the power of thermonuclear reactions. If this scientific problem—

the most complex in the entire history of science—can be solved, it will make available a new, practically inexhaustible source of energy. According to specialists in the field, this source of energy will be safer than the present generation of atomic power stations.

Back in 1978, at the request of the Soviet government, Academician Velikhov brought to the International Atomic Energy Commission a proposal for developing a thermonuclear reactor on an international basis. At this point Soviet scientists had worked out a promising new concept for such a reactor, which is the principle of the "Tokamak" structure.

On the twenty-sixth of May, a month after the accident at Chernobyl, the International Atomic Energy Agency held a conference in the Crimea on the technology of reactors.

In the opinion of Academician Boris Kadomtsev, "The creation of a thermonuclear reactor will require answers to a whole series of problems in the realm of physics, technology, and engineering. The scale and complexity of these problems demands an international approach to their resolution."

The "Tokamak" concept is one step on the path toward an incredible future for the energy industry: harnessing the power of the sun.

■ ■ ■

Q. What is the International Atomic Energy Agency?

A. This is one of the international organizations that belong to the United Nations. It was founded July 29, 1957. The charter of the IAEA states that this "agency strives to encourage the most rapid and widest use of atomic power for the maintenance of peace, health, and well-being on the globe." One hundred thirteen countries belong to this agency, including those that own atomic-powered electric stations.

The General Conference and Council of Directors forms the ruling body of the IAEA. This latter includes thirty-five countries, the Soviet Union among them. Since 1981 the general director of the agency has been Hans Biks of Sweden. The secretariat of the IAEA employs 1,750 individuals, of which sixty are specialists from the Soviet Union.

IAEA's main function is to prevent the proliferation of nuclear weaponry, and to act as a watchdog to prevent nonnuclear weapons states from switching atomic energy power stations over to military uses.

■ ■ ■

Q. What was the total material damage caused by the Chernobyl accident?

A. The national economy suffered great losses. The worst of these losses was the death of human beings and the irradiation of workers at the power station. But if we are to speak of material damage, the following losses must be mentioned. The Chernobyl nuclear power complex was shut down; in order to compensate for the lost energy, additional expenses were incurred. Four reactor units are worth 400 million rubles. As a result of the repair work going on at the complex, the start-up of several other electric stations is being delayed. The evacuation of people, the compensation for damages, the placing of technicians at the site of the accident, and the work itself on deactivating and cleaning up the reactor required large financial outlays. The people, resources, equipment, and so on used in the course of the clean-up have all been diverted from other spheres of the national economy.

According to B. Gostev, Minister of Finances of the USSR, total financial losses will amount to two billion rubles.

■ ■ ■

Q. Wouldn't it have been better to remove the nuclear fuel from the broken reactor for burial at some other site?

A. According to physicists, the most reasonable course is to not touch the fuel, but instead to bury it together with the reactor inside a sarcophagus. According to Mr. A. Petrosyants, president of the Government Committee on the Use of Atomic Energy, "The fuel remaining in the reactor does not present a threat; this conclusion is based on the laws of physics."

■ ■ ■

Q. What are the maximum permissible levels of radiation exposure for those working at the accident site?

A. The maximum permissible dose is 25 roentgens. Every person working at the site is equipped with a personal dosimeter whose meters are strictly monitored by the medical service.

There are various types of dosimeters. Some look like a ballpoint pen. Others are pendant accumulators made of aluminum. There are square dosimeters worn on the chest; they give off a rose-colored light in the presence of radiation.

The time one is allowed to work in the accident zone is also limited. When this limit is reached, all workers receive supplementary vacation time; during the course of working at the site, all receive a high-calorie, high-vitamin diet. Once the 25 roentgens have been accumulated, the individual concerned is forbidden to perform any sort of work involving elevated levels of radiation.

■ ■ ■

Q. At present how many hours are there in a working day at Chernobyl?

A. This depends (and depended) on the location of the work, its difficulty, and its danger. For example, a day's shift for the miners digging a tunnel towards the reactor was three hours. There were eight shifts in a twenty-four-hour period. Especially dangerous was any work performed directly next to the reactor: welders, for example, were limited to working for only a few minutes.

■ ■ ■

Q. Was the work on eliminating the consequences of the accident performed under coercion?

A. Coercion, no; obligation, yes. If you are referring to the firemen, policemen, and soldiers, for whom the obligatory fulfillment of orders has been the norm in all countries and in all times, this should elicit no surprise. It is true that in the first days of work during the evacuation of the local population and deactivation of the site a large number of people participated who were obliged to do so under orders. But from the very first day it became clear that what was needed was not so much a large number of hands as qualified specialists from a wide range of professions. These people were brought to the reactor site on an entirely voluntary basis. As to workers who had been on the job at the Chernobyl power plant before the accident, three thousand were immediately relieved of their duties after the accident and left the station. Only those who were willing and able to remained.

There was no shortage of help, whether at the station or in the accident zone. The headquarters in command of the clean-up were unable to accept the help of everyone volunteering to participate in the operation. Thousands of telegrams were received from volunteers. Many people came on their own initiative and worked free of charge during their vacation time. Which shows that volunteers were attracted not merely for the pay, although it is true that salaries for work performed in the accident zone were quite high. The more complicated, responsible, or dangerous the work, the higher the pay scale. Needless to say, medical control over all categories of workers was equally strict.

■ ■ ■

Q. Was any new technology used in the course of the clean-up work? If so, what kind?

A. First of all, the equipment already on hand was refitted; the cabins of tractors, helicopters, bulldozers, and cranes were shielded with lead plate and hermetically sealed. This was essential for protecting people from radiation. Buses used to transport workers through dangerous areas were also shielded with lead.

Later on they began to use more complex technologies at the accident site: robots and remote-control mechanisms of various types. Unfortunately, the high ionization of the surrounding air often disabled these complex machines, causing their accumulators to run down.

■ ■ ■

Q. How many years will the sarcophagus stay in place?

A. For hundreds of years. In the opinion of Academician V. Legasov, "Perhaps our descendants, providing that there is a need to do so, will find a means to remove it all to some other location or to totally neutralize it."

■ ■ ■

Q. Will the sarcophagus allow radiation to escape into the atmosphere?

A. The only thing that will enter the atmosphere from there is heat. The cement structure provides for the total isolation of the radioactive fuel; it incorporates a safe ventilation system and the thorough cleaning of contaminated air.

■ ■ ■

Q. Isn't the burial of radioactive wastes in itself a crime against nature?

A. According to one school of thought, the wastes of the atomic power industry are, from the ecological point of view, the least dangerous. All other branches of industry discharge their waste products into the surrounding environment. Nature, however, must not become a huge dump where we leave industrial wastes. Atomic power plants do not throw away their waste materials. Instead, they are solidified, usually in the form of glass or ceramics, which eliminates the possibility of contact with the environment, and held safe in special "burial grounds."